ONE BEING ONE

One Being One

John Davidson

Science of the Soul Research Centre

Published by:
G. P. S. Bhalla, Secretary
Science of the Soul Research Centre
c/o Radha Soami Satsang Beas
5 Guru Ravi Dass Marg, Pusa Road
New Delhi 110 005, India

For internet orders, please visit:
www.ScienceoftheSoul.org

For book orders within India, please write to:
Science of the Soul Research Centre
c/o Radha Soami Satsang Beas
BAV Distribution Centre, 5 Guru Ravi Dass Marg,
Pusa Road, New Delhi 110 005

First edition 2010

17 16 15 14 13 12 11 10   8 7 6 5 4 3 2 1

ISBN 978-93-80077-09-3

Printed in India by: Lakshmi Offset Printers

"Rabbit's clever," said Pooh thoughtfully.
"Yes," said Piglet, "Rabbit's clever."
"And he has Brain."
"Yes," said Piglet, "Rabbit has Brain."
There was a long silence.
"I suppose," said Pooh, "That's why
   he never understands anything."

A.A. Milne (Winnie the Pooh)

Off and on, in some rare moments of our
spiritual life, the soul becomes aware of
the presence of the Divine. A strange awe
and delight invade the life of the soul, and
it becomes convinced of the absoluteness
of the Divine, which inspires and moulds
every detail of our life.

S. Radhakrishnan

PUBLISHER'S NOTE

Science of the Soul Research Centre publishes books about spirituality. It promotes understanding of the common spiritual Power that lies at the heart of all life. It encourages exploration of the inner journey of spiritual experience, the essence of which is the same for all human beings, regardless of their creed, colour, country, culture or language, or of the time in which they lived.

SSRC books seek to dissolve the barriers between religions. Importantly, the SSRC imprint aims to explore spiritual truth from diverse perspectives. It allows for personal perspectives, inferring that although there are as many nuances of expression as there are individuals, all, at their depths, converge towards one shared Reality.

One Being One presents a reconciliatory perspective within the current dialogue between science and religion. It is hoped that it will contribute to a better understanding of these two fields, which are so often presented as contradictory.

CONTENTS

CONTENTS

SPEAKING PERSONALLY

For as long as I can recall, three interwoven strands
have been a part of the fabric of my life. A love of
nature, a sense of the mystical, and an appreciation of
science. As a child, whenever I was free from studies,
and weather permitting (or even otherwise), you
would find me in the meadows, among the hills, by
the seashore. What drew me was as much the peace
and magic of nature as an interest in all the other lives
going on around me. The sun on early morning dew;
the contented clucking of chickens foraging in the
farmyard; the swarms of painted, dancing butterflies
on the buddleia; the intricate perfection of a spider's
web. I can remember singing out loud with the pure
joy of it.

When my mother gave me a small plot of
ground to garden, much to her horror, I planted simple

wildflowers – dandelions, daisies, and no doubt other more noxious 'weeds'. Years later, when I had a home of my own, and long before it had become the conservationist 'thing to do', I did the same. Now we have an abundant wildlife garden, pond, and wildflower meadow.

One learns much from observing nature. The beauty and the harmony, the cooperation as well as the conflict, insights into the mind and language of other creatures, the amazing world of instinct. Breathtaking happenings, soul-expanding moments, glimpses of other worlds lived alongside one's own.

As I moved into my teenage years, and began to think about the hidden meaning of life, I realized that my love of nature came from a deeper source, and I began a more inward quest. What is life? What is death? Why do things happen in the way they do?

At Cambridge University, studying biological sciences, for the first time in my life I met like-minded people, and began to read more deeply. It was both a relief and an inspiration to realize that my experience of life had been shared by many more before me. I remember attending a Buddhist lecture at King's College, and was much impressed by the atmosphere emanating from the monk who gave the talk. He recommended doing at least five minutes meditation every day, but suggested no technique.

In my reading, I came across a technique using a *mantra*, and tried it out. The results were remarkable, but I knew I needed more guidance. And so, more thinking, more searching, until – not long after – I came to know about a certain spiritual master, Maharaj Charan Singh, in India.

I felt pulled and called beyond all measure. It was not just the spiritual dimension of his teaching. All my life I had been fascinated with India. I knew Rudyard Kipling's jungle stories backwards and, from a very early age, Tom Corbett's *Maneaters of Kumaon* had thrilled me with its atmosphere of the jungle and Indian village life.

And, not long before hearing about Maharaj Ji, the chance reading of a translation of the songs of the Indian mystic, Mirabai, on the back of a record sleeve had unexpectedly set my heart aglow. "My consciousness has expanded to meet the one Lord, and now I care nothing for what the world may say," sang the Rajasthani princess so long ago.

I received initiation from Maharaj Ji one Saturday in February 1967. The following week, I started my first real job at the Department of Applied Mathematics and Theoretical Physics at Cambridge. Although my degree was in biology, I was helping with the computer side of an applied maths research project.

It was my first introduction to computing, which, as time passed, became my profession. There was experimental work, as well as the first use of computers in the classroom. They were pioneering times.

I was now working in a scientific environment, where we discussed and talked about things with each other. In the same department, Stephen Hawking and other well-known personalities were also at the start of their careers. On Stephen's office door, I recall, was the enigmatic note, "Black holes...are out of sight." As the years went by, I became increasingly interested in the ongoing dialogue between science and religion, which – in my own mind – I automatically expanded into science and mysticism.

It seemed to me that the universe – inner and outer – was one, and that human perspectives on it were all part of one picture. That being so, the mystical and scientific perceptions of life must be compatible. But it takes time for one's understanding to mature, and it was not until 1984, when I left the university to run a small business, that I started putting pen to paper, trying to express how the scientific and mystical perspectives on the universe were by no means incompatible.

The result was a series of five books that were published between 1987 and 1992. Rather than adopt a philosophical approach, I did what came naturally to me, and looked at nature. I addressed subtle energy phenomena, observed relationships between the body as described by yogis (from within) and the same body as described by scientific analysis (from without). I looked at the intriguing world of new physics, how everything is just a dance of energy, spun out in space, as mystics have always said. And I returned once more to my love of wildlife – the host of other creatures with whom we share our planet, their lives, their minds, and the manner of their evolution.

5

And it seemed to me that while the scientist looks at the outer universe with the help of his analytical intellect, the mystic explores the inner universe of the very consciousness that scientists use to perceive the outer world. Both are looking at the same one universe, the only difference being in the perspective and the field of study. And naturally enough, I found that there was no incompatibility between the two seemingly so different worlds. In fact, I came to the conclusion that a study of the inward world of consciousness – which includes the primary tools of science, the mind and intellect – illuminates science in a way that nothing else can.

Concurrently with my scientific studies, I had developed an ever-deepening interest in the world's spiritual and mystical traditions. This study became more focused when, in 1989, Maharaj Ji asked me to research the origins of Christianity, and to write a book on the original teachings of Jesus. At the same time, I was asked to take on board the organization and rewriting of an extensive glossary of Indian mystical terms.

I set to work with considerable enthusiasm, but then, in June 1990, in an event that to me was entirely unexpected, Maharaj Ji left this world. The sense of loss was almost unbearable, but not long after Maharaj Ji had departed, his successor, Baba Gurinder Singh, called a number of people together, and told us that he wanted to expand the scope of the 'glossary' to include all spiritual traditions. I then realized that with his usual undemonstrative foresight, Maharaj Ji had set me up with a lifetime's work before he left.

For some years, I worked on the two projects side by side – Christian research, and wider research for what became the multivolume *A Treasury of Mystic Terms*. The fruits of the first project, *The Gospel of Jesus*, were published in 1995, and the first six volumes comprising Part I of the *Treasury* in 2003. Part II is presently nearing completion.

Back at the end of the 1980s, after completing the five books on science and mysticism, there had remained in my mind one further book. A more specifically mystical book, which laid out the mystic path as I understood it, and which summarized, in simple language, the relationship between the scientific and mystical traditions. Over the years, the prospective content of this book evolved, until it finally took shape in the present volume.

One Being One is thus a distillation of many years of thought and study, and evolution of understanding. It has brought me back to my personal spiritual roots, to the three strands that have been woven into my life – nature, science, and mysticism. It is from a great love of all three that this book has been written. And with the realization that books are at best only pointers, and not to be taken too seriously, I have tried to write in a simple, light-hearted, as well as occasionally humorous and sometimes lyrical manner.

Yep, this is the introduction, so if you generally skip them, now's the moment. But if you like to know the context, here's where to find it.

One Being One falls naturally into three parts. The first retells an ancient story – the perennial and universal spiritual or mystical philosophy. The second looks at some aspects of this philosophy in the context of everyday human life. The third relates it to some primary aspects of one of the prevalent belief systems of present times – the scientific worldview.

It is, by design, a short book, and the intention has been to present only an overview and an introduction to the matters under discussion. Something to suggest a spiritual way of looking at ourselves and the world around us.

The essential theme running throughout is the common denominator and harmonizing thread linking all aspects of existence – the dimension of being, consciousness, or spirit. It is called universal because that is exactly what it is. It is present in all beings, human or otherwise, and it pervades the entire universe. It is the One – the One Being, the One Spirit, the immanent divine presence.

As human beings, if we can understand something of this universal Spirit of which we are all a part, it will change our lives and the way we interact with each other. In a world of increasing globalization and multiculturalism, an understanding that all human beings share a common spiritual heritage would seem to be an answer to so many problems. It is a realization that transcends religions and belief systems, and all human divisions of wealth, social status, education, intelligence, and the like. At the same time, it honours and respects the colourful and variegated pageant of the global human society. Wherever and whoever a person may be, they are all a part of the One Spirit, the One Being. No one is excluded. Indeed, all possess the potential to realize their inner identity with this One Being.

When it comes to the world of science, an understanding of this universal spiritual perspective is something that is largely missing. Yet, when it is brought into the picture, it helps shed light on a number of basic conundrums. On the whole picture, actually.

And because the scientific worldview is so prevalent in present times, this introduction concerns itself largely with the scientific perspective, a subject addressed more specifically in the latter part of the book.

It must be understood that science, as an explanation of "life, the universe and everything", is only another belief system, another way of looking at things. There is a significant difference between science as a means of understanding, manipulating and utilizing material forces and science as a description of the ultimate Reality. These two aspects of science, however, are rarely distinguished, and these days the one is commonly mistaken for the other.

Modern science suffers from the lack of an inherent spiritual perspective. No one can deny that the last 150 years have witnessed incredible technological advances. Yet these achievements have led to the rape and wreck of our planet in a previously unprecedented manner. It seems to me that if science had possessed a foundation that had given it an intrinsic moral, ethical and spiritual perspective, we would never have travelled so enthusiastically down this road of self-destruction.

Individual scientists may possess deep ethical, human and spiritual understanding, and there is no doubt that many take the consequences of the application of scientific discovery very seriously. But science as a logically consistent description of the mechanics of the material universe rigorously excludes anything but raw empirical data and intellectual theorizing thereon. This need not be so.

Recent years have seen the rise of the Intelligent Design movement, which proposes that evolution and other natural processes are driven by a higher Intelligence, rather than by chance and natural law.

Much depends, of course, on how you perceive the nature of this 'Intelligence', but the idea has unfortunately been taken on board by religious fundamentalists, eager to provide proof of a creationist belief system drawn from *Genesis*. That makes no sense to me, but the idea of nature being permeated by an essential Intelligence or Consciousness that gives rise to all the natural 'laws' and 'principles' known (and unknown) to science does not seem like such a bad idea. After all, these 'laws' must originate 'somewhere' beyond the confines of space and time. But whether we call this Intelligence 'God' or 'Nature' or anything else makes no difference to the existence of the universe. And our conceptions of this unseen Intelligence are bound to be somewhat limited.

Sadly, the espousal of Intelligent Design by 'six-day' creationists has resulted in a head-on confrontation with neo-Darwinian, 'nothing-but-chance-and-matter' evolutionists, and a consequent polarization of positions. The result has been an entrenchment in old ideas on both sides of the divide, and we now have fundamentalist scientists as well as fundamentalist Christians.

But, as futurists say, "The weak signals of today give rise to the strong signals of tomorrow," and I suspect that there are probably some elements of Intelligent Design that will in future be incorporated into the accepted view of the evolution or constant change among the species.

13

I guess that what really needs to shift is an understanding of the actual nature of the 'Power' or 'Intelligence' pervading nature that has given rise to such a well-ordered universe. It may be staring us in the face, but we are still not seeing it. That is largely what this book is all about.

One Being One, then, is an overview and a general mystical perspective on "life, the universe, and everything". And so far as I can see, there is no conflict here with good, definitive, evidence-based science. After all, true mysticism is the quest for a higher Reality, and that also entails a clear, direct and honest appraisal of the physical universe and our relationship to it. It also requires an intensely honest and focused examination of one's own self, in order to uncover the true nature of that self.

So, while science is the study of matter by mind, mysticism is the exploration of consciousness by consciousness. And though both are dedicated to the quest for truth, there's bound to be a difference in the methodology. But this in no way invalidates either one or the other. Not only can the two co-exist peacefully, but the one can draw strength and inspiration from the other.

Put another way, you could say that there are two ways of trying to understand the universe. There's the scientific, rational, analytical, and objective view that regards the material universe as the only reality. And there's the subjective view that seeks beauty, truth and meaning, looking to find a higher Reality in the sphere of being or consciousness. There is nothing incompatible between the two. In fact, in one sense, they are already united, for the objective view only exists within the subjective consciousness of the observer. It seems to me that science would be greatly enhanced were these two viewpoints to merge into one perception of the Whole. Indeed, some forward-looking folk reckon that this is the direction in which science is developing.

I have to admit that what is written here often relies on *a priori* reasoning, on taking certain things for granted. I've tried to present things in a logical manner, but I do presume the existence of an all-pervasive, unseen Being or Intelligence. But then many scientists presume the material world to be an independent, external, self-created and self-organizing reality. That is also *a priori* reasoning.

Everyone has to have some starting point which they take for granted. None of us start with a blank page. We all bring our individual minds and psychologies to bear upon whatever comes within our orbit. In fact, it seems to me that you cannot (by reason) prove or disprove the existence of a higher Intelligence. We begin with a belief or feeling, which we then try to substantiate or justify by reasoning.

One final point. Though you'll find some acknowledgments at the end, I decided to dispense with endnotes, references, bibliography, and all that sort of stuff. They make a book dense. And these days, with the prevalence of the internet, it's so easy to find whatever you are looking for. Except Reality, of course.

THE
BIGGER PICTURE 17

ONLY ONE

There was no place, there was no time,
Only He dwelt within Himself;
He alone, and One complete:
Just Him, no other, only One.

He was but Love, and only Love;
'Yet, of Himself, He only knew –
A hidden treasure, known to One:
Just Him, no other, only One.

A desire surged within the One;
He in Himself perceived Himself,
Wanting only to be known:
Just One, no other, only One.

The desire gained strength,
Resolve, and will;
Then a Song formed within Himself:
One Song, no other, only One.

The Song went forth,
It sang and played;
Music made form within the One:
Still One, no other, only One.

Form made forms;
They grew and danced;
An image each, within the One,
Of One, no other, only One.

But, as they danced,
The forms forgot
The One within who made them dance:
Still One, no other, only One.

Yet some considered, as they danced,
Whether there might be somewhere,
Some time, some place, somehow,
Some One, no other, only One.

The Hidden Treasure smiled within,
His purpose now come into view;
He bent His Song to sing to them
One Song, no other, only One.

They heard the Song,
Received the Call,
And, listening intently, sang
His age-old Song, no other, only One.

And now, the treasure all around –
Love's Song sings no other sound –
The images in One have found
There is no other, only One.

There is no place, there is no time,
Only He dwells within Himself;
He alone, and One complete:
Just Him, no other, only One.

THE
MYSTIC STORY

GETTING THINGS STARTED

Before the beginning, there was Stillness. Silence. No time, no space, no thing. Nothing of the things that we comprehend in our minds. There was no mind, no body, no sky, no sun, no stars, no galaxies. No physical universe at all. No astral or causal heavens, or anything of that sort either. No proprietary Jewish, Christian, Muslim, Buddhist, or Hindu heavens. Absolutely nothing. Any where. Any place. Any time. Except Stillness. And Stillness was Conscious Being. Stillness existed within Itself, for Itself, of Itself. And Stillness was Love.

According to the Muslims, Conscious Being was a Hidden Treasure. How long He (let's call It that and be done with it – you can't call Love 'It', 'She' sounds ingratiatingly PC, and 'SHe' is just plain ridiculous!) – how long He had been hidden is a silly question, because there was no time by which to measure, "How long?" And no change in the Stillness, by which to measure time. But – so they say – the Hidden Treasure wanted to be known. Wanted to be loved. Wanted to experience His own love. So He created a creation. But out of what? Out of Himself. So simple!

In the beginning, He projected Himself, He emanated Himself, within Himself. For He was (and is) just One. The first desire of Love to be loved, to know His own love – that desire or will sowed the undifferentiated seed that sprang into two-ness, three-ness, and thence into manyness. He flowed out (or in?) within Himself, for there was (and is) nothing but Him, in all the many nooks and crannies of His created cosmos.

Some say He spoke, and His Voice formed all things. His Word resounded and the resonances made creation. Some say He sang, and within the symphony of His Music all things were formed. Some say He shone forth, and His Light wove the dance of forms. Some say He is pure Energy, and His Energy moved and vibrated, and so everything danced into existence. Some say He is a Father, and His only-begotten Son went forth, and did the work of creation. Some say She (ah well!) is a Mother, and within her cosmic womb all things have grown.

The poets say He is the Root of the Tree of Life growing in the garden of His own pre-eternal love. And its many branches, twigs and leaves are His creation. Or they say He is a Spring, or a River, or a Fountain of Living Water, which – flowing out from His eternal garden – watered the desert of nothingness, which sprang into abundant life.

The philosophers and metaphysicians say that He is the One Essential Being, the Source, the Origin and the primal Cause of all. By projecting His own Being within Himself, He formed, as it were, an Axis of Being, an Ontological Dimension (they like fancy words), within which all forms have their being. Everything is formed out of Being (or Consciousness), for there is nothing else. Oh, and they also say that He is Life, which is the same thing as Being or Consciousness; and so all the little beings live, and that's what life is. Or they say that the Silence was a Void, and from the Void all things have come.

Others have said that He is a Puppeteer. He takes all the puppets from His bag, He pulls the strings, and the puppets start dancing. Everything, they say, is just His play, His dance. "All the world's a stage." And when He's finished, He puts all the puppets back in His bag, and goes away. But how can there be a question of starting, finishing, and going away for the One who created time? Only puppets pose such questions.

So that was, so they all say, how He did it. And who – you may ask – are they? Well, there's the ancient Greeks, they said that. So, too, did the yogis and writers of the Hindu sacred books. And the Buddhists, too. Then, the Jews and the rabbis of the Kabbalah, they said much the same, using different imagery. And the Christians and gnostics, too ("In the beginning was the Word,...") voiced the same opinion. And, of course, the Sufis. And a host of native peoples who never felt the need to crystallize their beliefs in writing, because it was clear to them that everything is a part of the Great Spirit, who lives and breathes in all things.

And how does the Hidden Treasure love Himself in all of this? Because love attracts, and all the dancing puppets are forever attracted to their Creator. They are droplets of love, loving the Ocean of Love in which they dwell. And more than that. His dance only exists by virtue of the little beings that populate the dance floor, the little versions of Himself that we call souls. And that means us. All of us. Human beings, animal beings, bird beings, reptile, fish and amphibian beings, insect and creepy-crawly beings. Even bacterial beings, I suppose, for how else do you account for them? And probably vast numbers of extra-terrestrial (and very strange-looking)

beings, too. And of course the heavenly hosts of
angels, archangels, cherubim, seraphim, houris, devas,
devatas, ghosts and what not, and many many more of
that ilk.

And His love, of course, is the origin of beauty,
too. When the little beings look at something, and
think, in their own way, "Wow!", and love it.

And all the forms that danced out into created
existence when He spoke the Word, "Be!", will dance
back again, one by one, when He gives the call,
"Return!" And I guess that those who heed the call are
the ones we say are mystics, seekers, and wayfarers
on the Path. And naturally, they can be in any time,
place, religion, culture, workplace, bus stop, garden, or
anywhere else you care to mention.

And there's another thing. He didn't just make
everything, and then go off on holiday (where to?).
His kind of love, one must presume, makes no sense
unless it engages and interacts, and that's the kind of
creation He wants. Engaging and interactive.

So His Word, or whatever you care to call it, is
forever creating and sustaining everything in existence.
He is in the creation, and the creation is in Him. If
He withdrew His Word, everything would vanish, like
switching off a light. Through His Word, He is present
in every little (and bigger) particle of His creation. We

little beings live and exist like fish within the Ocean of His Being.

And if all the little fishes want to worry themselves silly, discussing whether or not such a thing as water really exists, well I guess that's just their – that is to say, our – problem, isn't it?

So here we are. The one big Being got a big idea, and here we all are. Lots of little beings all dancing about. Sounds cool! Life should be a breeze. All the little beings just bopping about, going wherever and doing whatever the big Being wants. And since He's all peace and love and stillness and wisdom, all the little beings are full of peace and love and stillness and wisdom, too. Right? Well, not exactly. I mean, look at us! So what went wrong?

That's a difficult question, because if He's the grand Puppeteer, then surely every move the puppets make must be by His intention and design. Can the puppets get ideas of their own, cut the strings that make them dance, and walk off the stage? Can the characters in a novel escape the author, and flee the page into a totally independent reality? It seems unlikely. So He must bear ultimate responsibility for whatever His puppets do, and however they exist. Yes?

But how so? He may be love, but just look at what His puppets get up to, and what happens to us. Hatred, wars, killing, disease, disasters, famine; arrogance, intolerance, stupidity, trickery, thievery, debauchery. That and a lot more. You name it. That's not love. But if everything is a part of His projected dance, surely He must be responsible for absolutely everything, good or bad? Not just the love, kindness, selfless service, forgiveness, humility, wisdom, and understanding bit.

And there's another thing. We puppets feel that we are self-willed and free, having individual identities. Most of the time, we don't feel like puppets at all. We feel as if we are doing everything ourselves. Until a tree falls on our house, an earthquake destroys our city, the stock market crashes leaving us penniless, our husband or wife leaves us, our children abuse us, disease takes away our health, and death finally removes us from the – er – stage. Not to mention the host of major and minor events that constitute our lives, and happen without our consent. In fact, we don't even know what's going to happen to us in the next two minutes. We are not even sure of what we are going to think next. That doesn't sound much like freedom.

So – umm – we feel we have a free and independent identity and will, and yet have little or no control over our lives. We didn't choose our parents, country, home, education, and so many other things that hem us round, and yet we insist that we are free. We are like pawns in a mighty chess game, trapped by circumstances way beyond our control or devising, yet still insisting that our moves are entirely those of our own free choice. I'd say that shows that we're in a pretty confused state of – er – mind.

33

Mind? That's something we all know about, but what is it? Maybe if we understood the nature of the mind, it would resolve a few of life's conundrums. After all, it is through the mind that we try to understand things. And what is this self that thinks that it is free?

Let's back up a bit. The little beings (that's us) were all nice and cosy, consciously and blissfully floating around as a part of the big Being. But somehow (and that must have been by His intention), we developed a sense of a separate individuality, of an individual self. And that's where things started to go wrong. As our sense of separateness and our involvement in the multiplicity of created things increased, so too did an unconsciousness or forgetfulness of the big Being. Until finally He was totally forgotten. And despite the fact that He continues to pull all the strings, and keeps the show going on, we puppets now regard ourselves as independent beings. We no longer believe in a Puppeteer, or if we do, our ideas concerning Him may be so wide of the mark as to have little meaning. And this sense of self is lodged in our minds.

So there are two primary factors contributing to the condition in which we human beings find ourselves – our mind and our sense of self. And of these, the mind is the more fundamental problem because it is the mind that generates the sense of self. Both are worth considering, but since our sense of self is so dear to us, let's start from there by asking the basic question, "Who am I?"

WHO AM I?

The most enduring and all-encompassing of mysteries must surely be the nature of life itself – especially the mystery of our own life and existence. Answer that riddle, one supposes, and the answer to all other mysteries will become clear. But what form will this ultimate answer take? Words? A book? Intellectual thought? It seems unlikely, for these are all a part of the mystery itself. And you can't answer a mystery with a mystery.

After all, what is language? What are thoughts? And more significantly, who is the one who's doing all this thinking and questioning? If we can't answer that, then all the answers framed in words and thoughts are related to a point of ignorance – ignorance of ourselves. So who is the one who is asking all these questions?

It seems pretty clear that we can never really get sufficiently outside ourselves to have a truly objective view on anything. We want to solve the riddle of thinking with our thoughts. We want to know the nature of our mind with our mind. We want to understand the nature of our self with our self. It's not rocket science to figure out that that kind of approach will lead us round in endless circles. It certainly is a puzzle!

Is there, then, another way to look at things? If we cannot get *outside* ourselves, can we get *inside* ourselves, and see things from another perspective? What can we say about our 'selves', anyway? Let's look at some fundamentals.

For a start, we are living beings. Conscious beings. We wake; we sleep; we dream. We imagine; we think; we daydream. We can sleep deeply; we can sleep lightly. We can even become completely unconscious. Yet even in the waking state, some folk seem to be more conscious than others. More aware, and more perceptive. Are there, then, levels of consciousness, levels of being? Can we expand the box of being we call our self, and become more conscious? And if so, how do we do that? Not by mental and psychological analysis, for that way will keep us at the level of the very mind and intellect that are conducting the analysis.

And surely we can fly higher than endless thoughts about our personality?

Then again, we are beings in flux. Our thoughts and emotions change all the time. The world itself continually changes all around us. Everything is in motion. The panorama presented to our senses, which makes up what we call our world, is forever shifting. Scientific experimentation tells us that even apparently static objects are constantly moving within themselves – and at incredible speeds, too. Inside of us and outside of us, everything is changing.

We perceive this constant flux as time. Yet time does not pass us by. We are forever in one moment – the now – perceiving change as time. Caught up in this constant change, we mostly live out our lives in memories of the past and concerns for the future. Yet the only moment that is truly real for us, that ever actually exists for us, is the present moment. But to learn to steady our being in this one true moment, to live in the eye of the storm, where all is peace in the midst of turbulence, seems like a massive undertaking.

But who is this I? Who is the one caught up in the travails of time? The body? No, you can lose bits of the body, without losing bits of your sense of self. And the body gets old, and wrinkled, and diseased, though the self may not. Are we our mind, then? That's getting closer. Our sense of self is certainly lodged in our mind. But it is forever changing. Thoughts, moods, desires, attractions, aversions, images, and all the rest of it, pass through our minds like a confused and never-ending movie, with many scenes unfinished and unresolved. And each, however fleeting, grabs the attention of our self. Temporarily and transiently, it becomes our self. "We pronounce it 'I', as if it were the whole of us, despite the fact that the very next moment, when external circumstances change, another 'I' has ousted it, and taken over control."

So do we even have a real and lasting self? Or are we, as the madman in the Christian gospels claimed, "legion, for we are many" – "possessed with demons", consumed by a myriad selves that do battle with each other inside our heads?

Wise men and mystics say that all these selves are just an illusion. Just a show, transient, having no lasting reality. All that truly exists is the One Being. He has made us as parts of Himself, and has projected this amazing and ever-changing show we call creation. Our reality, our true self, is the same as His. Our inner-most being (Sufis call it the 'secret'), our innermost consciousness, our spirit or soul, the essence of our existence – call it what you will – is the One Being. The 'legion' selves created by our minds are only imaginary demons (and angels, too), waiting to be exorcised and banished into nothingness as we awaken to our true spiritual selves.

So much of our sense of being is founded upon a mistaken sense of who we are, upon an ephemeral and ever-changing 'self', upon primal egotism. This is the essential characteristic of the human mind. So what then is this mind? It's clearly no small matter.

39

The cosmos, so the sages say, has been created by the One Being as an emanation of Himself. It has been projected out of and within Himself, as successive worlds or levels of creation, as a hierarchy of being.

According to some, in the course of this emanative process, mind first appears high up in this hierarchy as the primal architect of the duality that leads to the multiplicity in which we now find ourselves. At that high level in creation, we can call it the universal mind. And from that point onwards, every little being as it descends further into the creation has – so to speak – a little bit of this greater mind attached, through which it views creation.

Practically all traditions say that there are a host of heavens or worlds ("many mansions", "all the worlds") in the creation, of ever-decreasing subtlety.

These realms are levels or stages in the hierarchy of creation. And as the little beings descend, they are equipped with minds (and bodies) suitable for functioning in those realms. It's an automatic process. And right down at the bottom of this hierarchy, there's our familiar, physical world.

We would certainly agree that where we find ourselves right now, we have a mind and body. No denying that. But in the process of communicating with the physical world, we have become so increasingly identified first with our mind, and then with our body, that we have forgotten our innermost essence, our innermost secret. We have forgotten that we are all little beings dwelling in His big Being. Some folk have called this forgetfulness, the Fall. First, we were all cosy, living in the blissful, eternal garden of the One Being. Then we got involved with mind and duality, and now look at us! No wonder they cast the mind as a deceiving serpent.

The human mind, being a part of the greater mind from which all this duality and activity originates, is attracted by multiplicity and diversity. This, however, makes it very unhappy, and to fill the vacuum of its own unhappiness, it seeks further diversity. It tries to find happiness in all the changing things around it – pleasures, possessions, and attractions of every conceivable kind. Of course, things that change can't bring any lasting happiness, and so the mind gets even more frustrated, restless and miserable.

In this manner, entangled in its own illusions, the mind further develops its sense of a separate identity, which it believes to be real. It identifies completely with its own thoughts, feelings, and bodily experiences. It even starts to think that it is nothing but the body itself. Thus, the apparent isolation of the little beings from the one big Being is complete. And in their distress, the little beings create mayhem, and suffer even more as a consequence. And that is what we call human existence.

Wait a minute! That's all very well, you may say. Maybe that's the way it is. Maybe not. But there's a great deal of unsubstantiated doctrine wrapped up in all of that, and one way or another, we common or garden human beings have to get through our daily lives. That's the reality we know. And that's definitely no metaphysical doctrine. That's humdrum, nitty-gritty, everyday existence, isn't it?

Well, let's have a closer look at this everyday existence. Perhaps its most obvious feature is change. Life is changing; things are changing. Everything is always on the move. Change is something you can rely on. We're always busy dealing with it. And as we try to keep pace with it all, we get distressed, and lose our cool. Our minds start shifting, prompted by all the change without. Emotions, moods, thoughts, feelings, desires, likes and dislikes, all pass through our minds in an endless conveyor belt of confusion, all clamouring for our attention. Ceaseless mental and emotional chatter. And, whether we realize it or not, that is suffering. So what's the solution?

Some say the answer to all this excessive busyness is a retreat. Get away from it all. Cool down a bit. Well, going on a retreat might help for a while, and give us some breathing space to see things in perspective, but change goes on wherever we are. And we take our minds with us wherever we go, as well. So there's a clue. Maybe, the essential key to peace lies not so much in tranquil surroundings, as within ourselves. Maybe we've got to address ourselves. Maybe we've got to face our own minds.

If it is movement and change in the mind that causes distress, then if we could only control and still our own minds, maybe we would solve all our problems. That way, we could find stillness in the heart of busy-ness. Our body is like a house in which the mind dwells, all tangled up with our primal essence of being, our soul. But whatever commotion is going on outside the house matters little, if it is peaceful within.

But first of all, we have to acknowledge that we can't control our own minds – something that's not too difficult to demonstrate. Just try repeating the phrase "Who am I?", silently, in your mind for five minutes without letting your thoughts wander off into other things. Or choose any other word or phrase that appeals to you. Do it with your eyes shut, to avoid external distractions. You will find that unless you have practised this kind of thing, you'll be lucky to repeat your chosen *mantra* for more than a minute without your mind heading off in several other directions. So much for the "I'm in control" image we might have had of ourselves. But to acknowledge that we don't have much control over what goes on inside our head is a major step on the road to self-discovery.

47

So what's to be done about it? How are we going to regain some inner control of ourselves? Well, it's not a new problem, and there's no new solution. The mystical traditions of the world's many religions and cultures have all sought similar means to this end. We're talking about meditation, of course. Or contemplation, or interior prayer. It's been given many names, and these days everybody's heard about it. Even doctors, sports coaches and business executives recommend it to help you relax and to be more productive. And the basic idea of meditation is to find our own centre of being, within ourselves. For in that centre lies stillness and silence, blissful peace and joy, and relief from all the frenetic activity going on around us.

It doesn't matter who you are, where you come from, or what you believe in, people of all times, places and cultures have tried to bring their minds to a point of stillness, so that they can regain contact with the essence of being within themselves. The little being that is a part of the one, big, silent Being. This is fundamental human stuff, way beyond all external differences and doctrines. All our problems are resolved if only we can once again regain contact with the One Being. If we can only climb back up that Ladder of Being to the One Source.

And for that, we have to learn to really live. And actually that means learning to die.

DYING TO LIVE

Death. The one certainty in life. The last great adventure. What is it? What happens? What dies? Is it complete extinction of everything, or does something survive the death of the body? Is it something to fear? Is it something to enjoy? Can you prepare for it? Can you learn to go through the process of death while still in bodily existence?

We'd started talking about meditation, so let's take it from there. How do you meditate? Well, it's all a question of focus, of concentrating the mind. But where, and how? Some folk focus on a candle or a statue, some on their breathing, others on various energy centres within the body. Others try to still their minds absolutely. A complete blank. No thoughts whatsoever. Some add various ascetic regimes to their practice – fasting, staying awake at night, and so on.

Some try chanting. These are all valid techniques for achieving particular goals. But not all roads lead to Rome. Why should they? (Whoever thought they did must have been a disoriented Roman.)

To experience, in meditation, the process of dying, the attention has to be focused in the centre of the forehead, a little above the eyes. Since we take it for granted that the head is the seat of mental activity, it makes sense to try and focus the mind there in meditation. When the attention is fully and completely concentrated at this point in meditation (by repetition of a *mantra*), we become unaware of the body. All consciousness is withdrawn from the body. Our little being then leaves the body and rises up to higher levels of being or consciousness. Our soul leaves the body through a sort of 'door' or 'gate' in the forehead, and enters a higher level of consciousness.

Some traditions call these higher levels of being, heavens. Just as this world is a state of mind, a level of consciousness, so too are the heavenly worlds. And that's the process of death. The focused consciousness rises up from the body and passes through the 'gates of heaven', also called the 'gates of death'.

Naturally, when the body really dies, the kind of place we go to depends very much on the kind of mind we have. It seems reasonable that a loving mind will go somewhere loving. And a mind full of hatred, negativity and material inclinations will end up some place reflecting that. Fair's fair! As in life, so in death. We go where our mind takes us.

So that's the start of meditation. To learn to die while living. To pass consciously through the gates of death before the body actually dies. "Die before you die." But to get such a degree of focus that we can come to understand death is not so easy. It can take a lifetime, because it entails dealing with all the stuff we've accumulated in our mind that prevents full concentration. The mind has to be purified of all material and outgoing inclinations, of all thoughts of self, of everything but the One Being. And achieving that is no joke. We have to face our own psychology – to come to know everything that is going on inside our head, much of which is presently unconscious, and awareness of which will probably make us feel uncomfortable.

So meditation involves a great deal more than simply sitting down with your eyes shut, and mentally repeating some verbal formula. It is the primary means of spiritual evolution, of spiritual growth. It is a shedding of all that obscures the light of our inner being. It becomes a way of life that includes the development of inner understanding, as well as learning how to conduct ourselves with grace, kindness, compassion, and love. Everything that goes into the making of an excellent human being, full of all the best human qualities, is to be rediscovered. "Be ye therefore perfect." We are to learn to live as the spiritual beings we actually are, as sunbeams of the great Sun, drops of the great Ocean. To become continuously aware of the presence of the One Being within and without. And that takes time.

52

Only when our inner being is purified of all the rubbish does it become still, and capable of passing through the gates of death while still living. Then we can come and go from the body as we please until the time comes for our actual physical death – upon which, we gladly lay down the body, and step out in a higher world.

BORN AGAIN...
AND AGAIN?

Now here's the rub. In our present life, most of us don't achieve anything like the degree of purity required for dying while living. Our minds are too involved with material existence to muster sufficient concentration to be able to pass through the inner door.

During the course of our lives, we think and act and desire, mostly in an entirely scattered and unfocused kind of a way. All of this thinking and acting leaves impressions on our mind, and at the time of death, our head is still full of stuff related to ourselves and to our existence in this world. So what happens to us after death?

Well, we go where our mind takes us. We might spend time in some inner place, some inner level of consciousness or being, its degree of happiness depending upon the purity of our mind. But sooner or later – usually sooner – our mind draws us back to this world, and we are reborn. Reincarnated. Even transmigrated into non-human forms, if that's where our inclinations really lie.

And not only that, but the actions we made in life, all of which created lasting grooves or impressions on our mind, now rebound upon us, and form the fabric of our next life. Our past determines our future, just as it does in the present life. Indian mystics have called this the law of *karma*, the law of action and reaction, of cause and effect. Greek mystics called it the law of justice.

Now we're getting into some deep stuff. We're getting to understand something of the hidden processes of the universe, and how everything functions as a projection of the One Being. It's all a matter of cause and effect. The cosmic accountant (higher aspects of the mind, actually) keeps track of everything. And we reap what we have sown. Like it or lump it.

And can we escape from this cycle of birth, death and rebirth? Yes, say the wise ones who seem to know about such things: through meditation of a very particular kind. They say that liberation from birth and death (an ancient ideal) is an essential aspect of the journey to the centre of ourselves. That learning to die while living is only a starting point.

But what kind of meditation frees us from ever having to die again?

55

We need to backtrack a little. Remember how we said that the Silent One has projected everything, and now sustains it through His Word, His Song, His Music? That's the key. "In the beginning was the Word, and the Word was with God, and the Word was God. Without It was not anything made that was made." The One Being sings the universe into existence. He speaks His Word, and the creation comes into existence. "When He decrees a matter, He says to it 'Be!' – And it is!" And just as He is conscious Being, so is His Word or Music also consciousness.

This creative Word or Music is the dynamic, active power of the One. This is what brings things into being, and sustains their existence. The Word is the One Himself. It is also the essence of our own being or consciousness. And it is musical? It can be heard? Yes.

The creative Word is light and sound, which can be experienced within ourselves, not with material eyes and ears, of course, but with their spiritual counterparts. The divine light of the Word can be seen within ourselves, and the vibrations of the Word can be heard as the sweetest and most compelling music.

This is our salvation. Meditation, as we have so far described it, is only a preparation. To withdraw all consciousness from the body, and to focus the attention in the forehead is only coming to the railway station. We have yet to board the transport that will take us to our destination. That transport is the creative Music, and we board it simply by listening to its enchanting melody.

Some of the world's greatest composers and musicians may have heard this Music within themselves. But try as they might, they could never capture, in the music of this world, its heart-rending beauty, its wonderfully innate harmonies, and its consciousness-bestowing qualities.

This cosmic Music is the Axis of Being, the Axis of Love, the creative centre of the universe. It never stops. If it did, the universe would cease to be. It is the natural link between the One Being and the little beings who feel themselves to be separated. It is a blissful ladder to the One, a column of glory leading to the Eternal, an ascending stairway to the Infinite.

58

There is no higher kind of meditation than listening to this celestial symphony. It leads beyond all bodies, minds, birth, death, and everything else in created form. It is the Silent Music of the Silent One. It contains the essence of His primal Stillness. Therefore, to contact it, the body and mind must become absolutely still. After focusing the mind by repetition of a *mantra*, after stilling all wayward thoughts and inclinations, then comes the time to sit in stillness, without thought, waiting for the Music to manifest itself. It is always there. Without it, no being could exist.

Just as birdsong is present in the garden, even when our minds are too absorbed in cares and concerns to hear it, so too does the creative Music play on eternally in the centre of our beings, even if we are too distracted to be aware of it. We only have to listen. To become truly still and silent. Then we realize that it has always been resounding.

But how can we attain this state? How can we rediscover our link with the eternal Sound of the Silence? How can we hear the Music of Life? Well, like so much else in life, it helps if we can find someone who has already done it, and whose part it is to show the way to others. That means a spiritual master, a saint, a mystic, a sage, a wise one of the highest order, a "Word made flesh". Someone who's living with us, right now.

COOLEST
OF THE COOL

A backward glance at history reveals that the world
has always had its spiritual teachers. They have been
present in probably every country and religion. But like
all teachers, some are going to be more knowledgable
and proficient than others. In the world of human education, some teach kindergarten, some primary school,
some secondary, and some are university professors.
In the realm of spirituality, the best kind of teacher
or spiritual master is someone who has fully realized
the One Being within himself. For him, no mysteries
remain. He has his mind under complete control. He
has contacted the creative Music, and has ascended in
spirit to the One. Other masters and mystics may have
travelled some distance on the Way, but have not yet
reached the final goal.

Some folk have therefore called this highest of beings a perfect master; for he is a perfect man, a perfect human being, and having reached his destination, he is able to show others how to follow the path that he has trod. Some masters, it is said, have actually been sent from the One without ever having had to go through the travails of repeated birth and death. Others have seen it all, and have finally risen above it. Either way, all masters live in this world, and suffer its troubles and turmoil like the rest of us. But it doesn't bother them, because they can see it all for what it truly is. Nothing gets to them. Masters are the coolest of the cool. "Cool as sandalwood, serene as the moon are saints."

A master is an extraordinary, yet completely natural human being. To be around him can be so spiritually uplifting that people know intuitively that they are in the presence of someone very special. The way he speaks, the way he laughs, the way he does everything is unique. It reflects his inner condition. He can, in turn, be wise and perceptive, loving and affectionate, kind and gentle, humorous and witty, strong and masterful. He does fierce, tough and scolding, pretty well, too, and much else besides.

Every moment, within himself, he is totally present in the presence of the One. He carries no baggage with him from the past, and no concerns for the future. "My yoke is easy, and my burden is light." This means that he is totally aware, and totally free to live his life and to be loving in an entirely selfless manner. The best of human qualities are therefore manifest in him.

His mission is to teach those human beings who come to him how to contact and hear the creative Music he knows so well. He initiates them (baptizes them in the Holy Spirit, as some have called it). He tunes them inwardly to the creative Music, so that in time they too can come to hear it. He teaches them the practical details of meditation, and guides them every step of the Way. He is not a theorist, but someone who has learnt to control his own mind. He knows all the ramifications of the spiritual path, and all its pitfalls.

He is always the giver, too, one with the supreme Giver. He has arranged his life in such a way that he never needs to charge a penny for all he does. He gives materially, emotionally and mentally, and most of all, spiritually. He is a never-ending source of grace and divine inspiration.

His reality is the conscious creative Music, the Sound of creation, the creative Word, and as such he is with everyone at all times. But he takes personal care, so to speak, of those he has initiated. He teaches them how to live a pure and unsullied existence in this world, so that it can no longer exercise control over them, and drag them back. He is the door that leads the soul out of this world, so that it never has to return to live again in a physical body. Truly, he is a saviour.

THE
HUMAN STORY

65

Okay. So we've summarized what we might call the universal spiritual philosophy or mystic path. There is One Being, and He comprises everything. He is the essence of our true selves, and the cosmos is a part of Him. Everything is a projection or emanation of Him, and nothing exists apart from Him.

Under the influence of our minds, which give us a false sense of who we are, most of us lead pretty humdrum lives, sprinkled with occasional joys and punctuated by periods of trouble and distress. And, as a final insult, we are then held responsible for our actions, and end up going round and round in a cycle of birth after birth, not necessarily as human beings.

It's a tough life, but the good news is that the One Being can be contacted within by means of meditation or true spiritual prayer. This makes life much sweeter. In fact, with the right kind of meditation and the right kind of guidance, we human beings can even come to understand what death is all about (while still alive). And with a bit of luck, and a great deal of effort and divine grace, we can even escape rebirth, and return to the One Being. And that's the divine purpose in the whole affair.

So that's the basics, and for the remainder of this little book, we will look at how this take on things illuminates first some aspects of our human situation, and then some modern scientific perceptions of what life is all about.

And I suppose it should be made clear at the outset, that just as words and descriptions are quite incapable of conveying the experience of the beauty of a sunset or the taste of a carrot, so too are they utterly inadequate to truly convey the nature of the One Being and the spiritual or mystic Reality. This means that words can be both a hindrance and a help. So it's best not to get hung up on them – they're just noises in the air or marks on paper.

Umm...you've probably noticed. I've tried to avoid it. The God-word. The thing is that the word is so loaded that it's become a serious hindrance. "What's in a word?" we ask. But when it comes to the God-word – a great deal. It's amazing how much baggage can be hung on just one word.

Some clever folk ask, "Who created God?", and often the honest answer is, "We have." The ideas, conceptions, ideals and what not, with which the word God has been endowed, are almost entirely of human origin and conception. The God of religion has been largely conceived in the mind of human beings.

We've even gone so far as to consider that He has a particular name or names in one language or another, forgetful of the fact that a human word is just a sound or a sequence of letters to which – in our minds – we have ascribed a meaning. If you don't happen to speak or read that language, then that word has no meaning at all. And anyway, languages evolve and die. They, too, are human creations.

The One Being, the Silent One, is beyond all names and concepts. He is nameless. "The name that can be named is not the real Name." His big Being is the essence of our little being. Did we but know it, there is no difference between the two. He is what we are, and we are what He is. That means that He is within us, for us, of us. Any hint of an idea that He is 'out there', 'up there' or even 'in there' – that He is anything other than the essence of our own being – is fallacious. In fact, when we even conceptualize Him as our own 'essence', we have gone astray. He has got nothing whatsoever to do with any of our concepts. He's not what we think.

Yet, although we may think we understand all this mystical stuff about the One, and know that He is beyond all human conception, we may still cherish a concept in our mind of a God built somewhat in the image of our own cultural conditioning.

And if we put all our effort into trying to realize a mental concept, to feel the presence of an intellectual construct, then that concept will hold us back. Such concepts, held without our even realizing it, can unknowingly hinder us.

So let's call Him anything but God. Let's pretend we never even heard the God-word at all, and start from scratch in our understanding of the One Being. In fact, let's let go of any attempt to form any opinion or concept of what He is like. Let's admit that we can't understand Him. After all, the Buddhists get along fine without a concept of God, as we might understand it. They have no problem developing a deep spiritual life in the absence of a God-concept. They seek a state of being. *Nirvana.* But is there a difference between God and *nirvana*? Only in the realm of concepts.

And while we're on the subject, let's realize that all our other concepts are just that, too. Just mental hot air inside our heads. Just constructs. And that includes our concepts of heaven, hell, soul, reincarnation, the creation, and a bunch of other words we've largely avoided in this book because they're loaded with all kinds of cultural and religious stuff, and trigger a conditioned concept. Yes, and our concepts of the mind, the One Being, the Word, and so on – they are all just concepts. We can use them as tools, as communication devices, as ways of trying to understand things at a human level. But if we get to thinking that our concepts are reality itself, then we're on the wrong track. Or so it seems to me, in my conceptual mind. A description of something is not the thing itself.

Realizing that our understanding of God is mostly conceptual is significant when we get to thinking whether or not such a Power really exists. The existence, or otherwise, of a God is a question asked by everyone who wants to understand things for themselves. Yet the enquiry is rarely prefaced by a rigorous consideration of what we actually mean when we speak of God.

72

Just ask ten people what they understand by the word 'God', you will probably get ten different answers. Most will offer confused conceptions drawn from a mix of social, religious, cultural, and personal influences. Some will describe a God based upon religious beliefs and the reading of religious texts. Some might cast Him in an anthropomorphic light, as a God given to human emotions, liable to be pleased or to take offence at human conduct. A few might portray Him as a universal spirit or as a transcendent, absolute Reality. The varied conceptions will reflect each individual's mindset, but can never begin to touch the Reality.

We may know God by any name or understand Him by any concept – none will do Him justice. Many folk instinctively reject the God or gods of religious doctrine, yet consciously or unconsciously know Him by another name. As Nature, Beauty, Love, or simply as Something – unknown and universal, beyond all human conceptions and divisions.

Those who try to debunk the notion of a God sometimes take the easy way. It's very simple. First, you set up a straw God, choosing the most bizarre aspects of the many prevalent conceptions of the Divine. Then you set fire to it, taking the concept apart with the weapons of bald reason, cynicism, and ridicule. But it's a facile approach. Gives atheism a bad name. Anything can be 'proved' by setting up a ridiculous Aunt Sally, and then demolishing it. Many spiritually-minded people also reject such conceptions of the Divine, realizing that there is a far more intelligent way to understand the nature of the divine Principle at the heart of things.

Whether or not we believe in such a Power, a fair discussion of the matter requires proper consideration of the notion of God, of the one divine Being. And acceptance of the fact that should such a Being exist, then His nature is going to be far beyond the reach of human argument, discussion, and description.

In reality, proof or its absence play little part in whether or not we believe in the Transcendent. Heartfelt belief or non-belief in Him do not really arise from reason and logic, though they may be supported by it. They arise from awareness, consciousness, perception, and understanding. If we have an inner sense that there is something bigger than ourselves, holding everything together, then we will feel that we believe in a God, however we may conceive of Him. If we are so inclined, we may then try to justify that belief by reason.

But if we have no such feeling, and think that "life, the universe, and everything" provide no indication of the existence of a higher Being, then we will have no such belief, and may argue the case accordingly.

Of course, cultural, religious and social influences may also have a significant part to play in our belief or non-belief in God. And mere belief in the existence of a divine Power is not necessarily companion to a spiritual disposition. Belief needs to be transformed into awareness and experience. Yet whatever our beliefs or experience, it is important that we feel free to consider things for ourselves, and respectfully allow others to do the same.

Human life, spirituality included, is full of paradoxes and contradictions, real or imagined. A diamond may have many facets, each reflecting a different colour. Yet the various colours do not detract from its oneness. The ten blind men, who each got hold of a different part of the elephant, all described it differently. Yet their descriptions were all accurate, so far as they went. The fact is that mind and intellect have a limited sphere of activity and usefulness. Those who feel that "the answer to life, the universe, and everything" can be codified and explained in rational and intellectual terms have set out upon an endless journey. You cannot contain an ocean in a teapot.

So much of life is a matter of concepts, opinions, and perspectives. Everyone has a different take on things. Yet the world is full of self-appointed 'authorities' on every conceivable subject, who will gladly tell you how and what to think. Just give them a little prod, and you'll be lucky to escape within the hour (or two). They will argue with you, and try to convince you of their perspective. Give them less than half a chance, and they'll do all the talking. Did you ever meet someone who tried to convince you of someone else's viewpoint? Of a viewpoint he did not share?

It's all a question of concepts, opinions, and uncertainty. If things were completely clear, there would be no viewpoints, no discussion. So as soon as a person tries to convince you of something, you can be sure that, deep down, they are themselves uncertain about it. They have just never addressed their own uncertainty. And the less certain they are, the more they'll shout. When the argument is weak, shout louder! It's human nature. And in human affairs, there are few certainties, because the realm of certainty is beyond the sphere of human perception.

Therefore, to avoid being blown off course by every passing breeze, we need to learn to think for ourselves. There's no point in quarrelling with anyone, but we do need to assess things against our own inner touchstone of truth, realizing that we are dwelling in the realm of uncertainty. True freedom of speech may be a rare privilege in this world, but no one can take away our freedom of thought. To avoid getting into trouble, we may need to keep quiet about what we think. But we need never surrender the right to think for ourselves.

Even so, losing the right to say what we think is a step in the wrong direction. The modern 'buzzword' is political correctness. We're supposed to avoid saying anything that will upset certain groups or cultures. We are expected to conform to a particular social dogma. Well, there's no reason to go about challenging and disturbing others unnecessarily, but the idea has been taken on board by many of the world's 'authorities', especially the religious authorities, and is being used to suppress freedom of expression. But surely it is only fair that any individual or institution who takes it upon themselves to tell others how and what to think should be open not only to criticism, but also to ridicule?

Conflicting religious dogmas each claim to be the last word on such matters as 'truth', 'salvation', and 'God', as well as how to live as human beings. But these are such fundamental questions that they must be open to discussion, and to freedom of expression and thought.

And since – it has to be admitted – religious dogmas and practices include some of the most bizarre constructs of the human mind, surely it is simply a matter of human honesty and decency to permit questioning and criticism? And if someone wants to make fun of our beliefs and practices, why not? This would also seem to be quite acceptable, if not essential. It's a way of pointing out inconsistencies without getting into long debates. Why should we be so sensitive to criticism? Let's develop a little maturity.

After all, if Christian, Jewish, Muslim, Hindu, Sikh, atheist, and other belief systems are in conflict on the same basic issues, it seems reasonable to suppose that at least some of their doctrines are misguided. And given the significance of these issues, surely they must remain open to discussion? The more we give way to the dogmatists who claim their feelings will be hurt if anyone disagrees with them, the less freedom there is for everyone, and the more effort we have to make to maintain our own internal freedom of thought. But if we are to be held responsible for our choices by the cosmic accountant, we must remain free to exercise our right to choose.

We go through life the best we can. We have no idea why we were dealt the set of cards we were born with. We don't know why things – good, bad or middling – happen to us in the way they do. Disasters of all scales, from global to personal, come uninvited. Good things, too, are difficult to orchestrate, and often what we think desirable, when acquired, turns out to be a source of problems. Even if we regard reincarnation as a reality, we can't see the processes by which we are given our just deserts. Just about everything is hidden from our eyes.

And yet the sages tell us that we are held responsible for all we do. Strangely enough, that makes sense to us. Even in our legal systems, we are deemed responsible for our actions, and are punished for our misdeeds. Yet the cosmic accountant keeps a far more exacting record. All our thoughts and deeds are recorded – not in some heavenly tome, but in the soft, impressionable putty of our own minds. We are the ones who keep the detailed record, deep in our own unconscious minds. If we are unaware of this, it is because we are almost infinitely forgetful, not only of our own thoughts and deeds, but also of the One Being.

So, if we are answerable for all we think and do, we need to learn how to control our own mind, and how to think for ourselves. And we will have taken a huge step in that direction, if only we can become aware of His unending presence within ourselves. It will also be of significant help in dealing with all the suffering we encounter.

Probably the argument most commonly raised against the existence of a divine Being is the state of the world. If He's a perfect being of perfect love, in complete control of everything, how come there's so much suffering? It's a good question, and the absence of any satisfying answer has led many down the path of unbelief. That's understandable.

It's amazing how adept we human beings are at creating misery for ourselves and other creatures. True, there are many selfless and caring people out there who do their best to make the world a better place. Yet there are many others, too, who use their 'superior' human intelligence not to alleviate suffering, but to make it worse. The variety of ways we have invented for creating misery is remarkable for its ingenuity. Wars, feuds, jealousies, family disharmonies, competition of every kind; torture, rape, pillage; abuse, bullying, unkindness, prejudice; pollution, filth, and ugliness of every kind. The list sounds like it came from some hellfire preacher of eternal damnation, intent on exposing every last scrap of human iniquity. Except that it goes on around us all the time.

And as if that wasn't enough, we have to contend with disease, accidents, earthquakes, volcanoes, landslides, tidal waves, hurricanes, blizzards, avalanches, climate change, and a whole lot more. Even the happiest and most caring of people can suddenly find themselves deep in the mire for no apparent reason.

And it's not just human beings who suffer. All life suffers. Most life forms can only sustain themselves by killing other life forms. Simply staying alive is the primary aspiration of every living creature; yet all are destined to die, and very few die of old age. Fear, pain, hunger, and the danger of being eaten by someone else are constant threats. Most creatures compete with each other simply for survival, often with members of their own species. And human beings kill (and eat) them all.

The primary architect of all this mayhem is the mind. Fair enough. But that doesn't answer why the One Being did things in the way He did. Why should He have set up a system that results in so much suffering in the first place? Couldn't He have achieved His objective in some other way?

There is little likelihood of a rational human answer to the conundrum, for we are not dealing with a Being who thinks like us, or even thinks at all. We must presume that His wisdom, intelligence and consciousness are far beyond the ability of most of us to grasp. But let's pretend for a moment that we can look at things from His perspective. Humanly speaking.

83

He is all love, all consciousness, all intelligence. He is all one, and all alone. A hidden treasure known only to Himself. But love desires to share. Love needs someone to love. Therefore, the urge arose to create beings who can share in all the love He has. We've mentioned this before.

Through His Word, His Music, His divine Power, He has created a vast creation, level upon level of worlds within the orbit of His own great Being. To achieve this, He has created the mind to perpetuate the illusion of separation – to turn His oneness into an apparent multiplicity, creating relationships (that we call cause and effect) between the hiddenly connected but seemingly separate parts.

He creates coverings – bodies and individual minds – out of the substance of each realm in which the little beings find themselves. And each being starts to consider itself separate.

The realms of His creation are stepped-down degrees of His own supreme consciousness or being. In most of these realms, the little beings float around in the bliss of His love and being. Worship of the Divine is the most natural thing in their existence, for they are totally aware of their Origin. Though separate, they remain consciously connected to Him. They don't have to think about it. It is utterly natural to them. They are blissfully happy in their existence, having no desire to return to their original home. They are spiritual beings dwelling in the realms of spirit.

But far away, on the outskirts of His creation (so to speak), the One Being has created a different scenario. His masterpiece, perhaps. Here the separation from Himself is intensified by the soul's association with a deeply individualistic mind and the coverings of a material body. So dense are these coverings that the souls are no longer aware of the divine and loving presence that dwells within them, supporting, surrounding, and sustaining their existence. They feel that they are on their own, fighting a losing battle for temporary survival of their bodies and identities. Like a lamp that has been shrouded in many layers of dense, dark cloth, it seems as if the light has been extinguished.

We are talking of the physical universe, of course, a tiny part of the entire creation. A hellish place, actually, if the truth be told, though it is also full of beauty if perceived aright, for He is everywhere, and He is Beauty. And here the One Being has devised His highest purpose. Elsewhere in creation, all the little beings are happy, having no desire to return to Him. But here, the suffering ultimately becomes so intense that the little beings cry out, often unconsciously, for help, for mercy, for anything to alleviate the pain.

The source of all this anguish lies in the depth of the apparent separation. Yet it may take many lifetimes for a little being to relinquish enough of its self-interested focus on its own material life to start to wonder if there is more to life than the daily grind. And here, perhaps, lies the hidden purpose of the One Being. For when a little being starts to seek answers to the meaning of its life, it is actually responding to the presence of the One within who gives it its existence.

And somehow, by divine design, so the sages say, having experienced the extremity of separation qualifies the little being to travel the entire return journey to its Source. To set out upon the journey home, and realize its essential oneness with the Divine.

And this can only happen to a human being. It seems there is a mystery in the way in which human beings are put together. The "best of forms", the "image of God", the "divine human body" – these are some of the epithets given to the human form by the sages who seem to know about these things. In this form – not in the form of any lower physical creature, nor as an angel or as some other being dwelling in a higher heavenly realm – a little being can begin and

even complete the return journey to its Source.

The One Being has made a creation in which to experience His own love. "He worships Himself through us." "I was a hidden treasure, and I wanted to be known, so I created the world."

Separation from our Source, which is the origin of suffering and misery, is a sharp stone in our shoe. Sooner or later it makes us stoop to seek out the source of the irritation, and remove it. And so we return. This is the story of His purpose and design.

And does the story satisfy? Well, there must be some truth reflected in it or the sages would not have mentioned it. But like the man who fell into a well, we can either go on demanding: Who built the well? How deep is it? What is the manner of its construction? How come we fell into it in the first place? Will we fall into it again? Or we can take the help of one who offers to lift us out, and then see what the situation looks like.

But even while we are stuck down the well, in this far-off corner of creation, struggling to make some sense of it all, we have not been abandoned. The Divine is always with us. In fact, in reality, there is no far-off corner. He is always there, everywhere. And that's a reason for the greatest joy, wherever we may be.

The One Being is never absent. How could He be, when only He exists? Deep in the heart of every little being lies the big Being. The Silent One. He who cannot be named. And He is love. At the centre of every conscious being and at the heart of every inert particle of existence lies the same essence of love. And love means bliss and supreme consciousness. It is the essence of life and existence. Without it, we wouldn't exist. Every being, no matter who or where, has love. Can a wave exist without the ocean? A sunbeam without the sun?

We may have got ourselves into one heck of a pickle, become so wound up that we have forgotten what really makes us tick, but He is still there. The One Being giving existence to our little being. That's a part of His purpose in this whole affair, remember. Having created us, He has not gone off on holiday. He is waiting for us to turn to Him. And He is very loving, very intimate, very caring, very patient.

Without doubt, He has done a strange and inexplicable thing by creating the illusion of separate identity and free will – which He also honours by not forcing an awareness of Himself upon His little beings. Yet He constantly seeks opportunities to flood us with an awareness of His inner presence, if only we will acknowledge Him just a little. He has done everything out of love, so that He can love Himself through us. He cares for us, and is always ready to nudge us, to give us a gentle reminder of His presence.

His reminder can come at any moment, often when we least expect it. Maybe we are driving along a country road, just minding our own business, when suddenly the beauty of a shaft of sunlight breaking through the overhanging trees catches our heart, and turns it over with an unexpected joy. Then, suddenly, the whole of our being seems infused with a radiance that hints of the Unseen. The veil between this world and the next seems to have become like gossamer. Everything glistens and vibrates to a hidden harmony. We sense the unifying oneness coursing through all things, and present in our own heart. Something inside us starts to sing. For He has touched our being, illuminated us from within, and we are glad.

Or maybe we are in distress. Life has hurled its javelins at us, piercing our heart. We may even be wondering how we can go on. There is no clear way forward, and present circumstances are almost more than we can bear. So we contract in upon ourselves. The suffering makes us focus inwardly, and suddenly, like a light in the darkness, a breath of love courses through our inner being. It may bring tears to our eyes with its poignancy. We may not even understand its source, yet we are grateful for the respite.

Or perhaps we have been practising meditation for many years, yet seem to be up against a brick wall. How can we break through to the vast open meadows of being that we feel sure lie just beyond? Then, somehow, we just relax, and let go. And we find that what we had come to think was so far away and difficult to find is already in our possession. We were simply looking in the wrong direction.

Or maybe we need to develop greater inner depth and sincerity. And with the kind of love we find so hard to understand, He sends us pain and hardship. And without our knowing, He simultaneously sustains us. And we learn compassion. We come to a clearer understanding of what is important and what is insignificant. We become more humble, and that, we must admit, is always a good idea! We come to realize that He is always there for us, all the time.

Or perhaps our heart is dry, even disconsolate and, without our even thinking why, we pick up a book and happen upon a sentence or a passage that strikes us so precisely that our heart is suddenly set aglow with bliss, and love, and yearning. And inwardly, we are refreshed.

Or it could be an entrancing moment in nature, a picnic with friends at some beauty spot, a chance encounter, an inspiring conversation. In so many ways, each particular to our own selves, and to our own inner state at that time, He reaches out to us. Or rather draws us in – into the orbit of His love.

Human perceptions are all awry and very limited. When we think we have been abandoned, He may be protecting us. When we wonder where His help has gone, He may be supporting our every step. When we think we are unloved, He may be cradling us in His arms. When we think we can never be forgiven, He has already forgiven us, and is only waiting for us to forget ourselves and our guilt. When we think we have doubts, He may be deepening our faith.

Such is the magic of the love with which He tends us, and which He weaves around us. But since He Himself has given us this illusion of freedom and separateness, He plays the game of letting us slowly discover things for ourselves. Time is no problem for the Being who has created time. And in the end, we discover that we have never had a separate existence, but have always dwelt within the sanctuary of His love.

So we evolve spiritually. And as our consciousness expands, as our little being merges increasingly into the One Being, so we come nearer and nearer to what folk have called *nirvana,* enlightenment, God-realization, union with God, merging with the Ocean of Love. And when we experience Him within, we find Him everywhere. Then we come to understand that every thing and every place is sacred and holy.

A SENSE OF THE SACRED

Modern man has lost his sense of the Sacred as an immanent presence in his affairs. True, a glance at human history shows that we have always had more than a strong tendency for negativity and destruction. But until the advent of modern science, our understanding of the cosmos was always linked with a sense of the divine immensity. The rising of the sun, the coming and going of the seasons, life and death – everything was a mystery, understandable only in the context of a divine Being who involved Himself directly in nature and in human affairs. The acquisition of scientific knowledge need not have changed that, but it has. Now we see a universe permeated not by a divine presence but by natural laws, amenable not only to reason but also to technology, and tractable to the will of man. In such a scenario, ask some scientists, who needs a God? But the reality is that we have simply pushed back the boundaries of intellectual knowledge; we have not uncovered the fundamental truth.

Yes, we know a little about natural forces: about the sun, the planets and the stars, about the intricate dance of particles and energy at the heart of matter, about how the body functions, and much else besides. But that need never have dispelled our sense of the Sacred. It could so easily have enriched it. After all, we still don't know how all these 'laws' came into being; how we came to exist as conscious beings; where space and time, and all that sail in it, came from; and how all the particles and forces known to modern science exist in the way they do. In fundamental terms, we still don't know what makes the sun come up. We don't know the secrets of life and death. We don't even know the nature of our own self.

We are still faced with a primal ignorance. But now our ignorance has become so deeply hidden through intoxication with our own cleverness that we have become unaware of our ignorance. Even with the clear evidence that our understanding of things has all but wrecked the planet in less than a blink of cosmic time, we fail to see the reason why, and we feel powerless to prevent the approaching catastrophe.

Had we but retained a sense of the sacred presence at the heart of things, we would never have

embarked on this path of self-destruction. Many of
the native peoples of America, Australia, Africa, and
Asia have looked on aghast at the ravages wrought by
'civilized' man. Many of them once lived with a sense
of being surrounded by a Great Spirit. Yes, there was
much superstition, and unfounded belief. But is that
not true of our modern age too? The superficiality
of material life; the rat race of desire for possession,
status, and renown; the psychological imbalances that
modern people live with as a result of the unthinking
and unconscious chasing of ephemeral dreams that
can never be realized; the bizarre beliefs and practices
of religion; the dogmatic assertions of science regarding the material nature of reality. These are the modern
demons that dog our footsteps, robbing us of our
innate spiritual freedom and a sense of the Divine.

 Why do so many of us long for the wilderness?
What are we hoping to find there? Magic? Awe? A
sense of the Sacred? Yes, and we want to find ourselves,
too. For within our selves, we find a still presence. Call
it the One Being, call it God. Call it anything, or call
it nothing – it makes no difference. We cannot, in the
end, escape the One who sustains our life and being.

 Why did the early Christian monks leave the
distractions of the cities and head for the desert? Why
did the yogis and others give up worldly life, and seek

refuge in the mountains and jungles? To find solitude and stillness. To find themselves, and to commune with the divine presence.

The further we stray from our still centre, the more distracted and the more miserable we become, however clever we may be. The closer we are to our still centre, the more peace and happiness we will find within ourselves; the more we will find spontaneous happiness, even bliss, flooding our inner being, drawing us closer to the Sacred One. And with it comes wisdom and understanding. Once you've tasted that kind of bliss and known that kind of knowledge, you realize that it's worth far more than the sum total of all human knowledge. And it travels with you into death as well. That alone makes it a unique and priceless treasure.

THE
SCIENCE STORY

Some pages back, we did a reality check on concepts, especially in relation to things like God, soul, mind, heaven, hell, and so on. The same principle applies to all human concepts, including those of science.

It doesn't matter how complex the mathematics and the ideas, scientific theories are simply descriptions. That's why they work. If we observe some phenomenon, and describe it in mathematical terms, that doesn't mean that the description is the phenomenon itself. The two are fundamentally different. Tasting an orange is an experience, and all the descriptions in the world, no matter how complex, will fail to convey the experience of the taste of an orange. You've got to put it in your mouth to know its taste.

So even if we think we've found some universal principle, like a mathematical description of gravity, it's still only a description. We can't then say that this is a 'law of nature' that all phenomena must *obey*. It's only a description of nature – a human concept. Why should nature obey our descriptions, especially when we are prepared to admit that our conceptions and descriptions are incomplete? Gravity worked just as well before Newton and Einstein as afterwards. In any case, scientists have yet to provide a fundamental, all-inclusive description of gravity, integrated with descriptions of other natural phenomena, such as electromagnetism. And no one claims to know what gravity and electromagnetism – or anything else for that matter – really *are*. A verbal or mathematical description can never be the thing itself.

102

We have such well-developed and intellectually enticing concepts and descriptions of things that we mistake our concepts for the reality. And in the understandable and laudable attempt to construct one all-encompassing description or theory, we confuse our different conceptions, too. Like trying to integrate partial descriptions of the universe such as Big Bang theory, subatomic physics, the origins of matter, evolutionary change among the species, and the origins of life and consciousness into one glorious, all-embracing theory of everything. While these are entertaining ideas that appeal to us, it is easy to forget that they are just concepts. Just a perspective on things, just a viewpoint and opinion. Not the whole deal.

But let's take things one step at a time. Let's take a look at how the scientific fraternity sees things, and then examine some of the basic concepts by which they describe physical reality and the origins of existence.

SCIENCE
AND THE ONE BEING

The standard view of science (though I wonder how many scientists really subscribe to all of it in their private thoughts) is that correct understanding of the universe can only exist in the intellectual and conceptual analysis of good old material or sensory experience. If some experience seems to fall outside this framework, then (so it is said) either it doesn't exist, or it can be explained away as some neurological phantom of the brain. Like the mind itself, the primary tool of science.

Yet the fact is that without consciousness, there is no science. And all science is spun out in the mind, which is an aspect of consciousness. And if there is no understanding of the nature of that mind and consciousness, then all of science – indeed all of human knowledge – is related to a point of ignorance. If we don't understand the essential nature of who is asking the questions and coming up with all the answers, then the veracity of the entire edifice of question and answer is suspect. Or at least it's relative to a backdrop of essential ignorance.

And this is the human condition. It doesn't invalidate science or human knowledge. Far from it. It simply puts it into a wider perspective. Let's accept that we are using an instrument (the mind) to try and comprehend the realm of sensory experience (material substance) without our ever having understood the nature of the instrument. We have no idea how to calibrate our most fundamental instrument of enquiry. We don't even know what it is or how it works. Science is the attempt to understand something, using something we don't understand.

We found ourselves in this human situation at birth and, from a very early age, we started thinking. We hit the ground running, and many of us have never paused for detached reflection on who we are, what we are doing, how we are doing it, and where we are headed. From the very start of our lives, we just ape what everyone else is doing, and away we go. If we get clever, and think we have found a new answer to some question, we dine out on it for the rest of our lives. But do we know who and what we really are, and where our thoughts come from?

The scientific community has become such an exclusive club that scientists won't accept anything that is not presented in their own terms. And since their terms are entirely material, nothing is acceptable unless it can be proved in terms of material evidence. And since consciousness is immaterial, science excludes all experiences of consciousness from its consideration except sensory or material experiences. And this, despite the fact that all scientific understanding takes place in the immaterial mind. When science considers mind and consciousness, it only does so by analysing the electrobiology of the brain. It leaves no space for the personal, subjective exploration of consciousness.

Come on guys! We're going round in circles. We will never understand the essential nature of life and consciousness that way!

Science and technology have achieved much, but they have not provided fundamental answers to the conundrum of our existence. Confusion and uncertainty will remain for as long as we entertain the idea that ultimate answers can be found in intellectual and conceptual terms. Once it is understood that there is a forgotten or hidden dimension to existence – the dimension of being or consciousness – then things will begin to fall into place. If we don't understand the relative and limited nature of our human science and knowledge, then we will remain in confusion. Even if we insist that we have all the answers.

Just look at the outcome of our great scientific adventure. A wrecked planet in just 150 years! Doesn't it indicate that we've missed the point, somewhere along the line?

All of science is illuminated by the simple understanding and realization that the fundamental characteristic of existence is not material substance, but being or consciousness. Everything is a projection of consciousness. This entire material universe, and a multitude of heavenly realms, too, are all levels of being or consciousness.

That may seem like too much to swallow, but doesn't it seem odd that while theoretical physicists are quite willing to entertain ideas of an infinite number of worlds wrapped up in hidden dimensions of space, the idea of multiple worlds lying hidden in higher dimensions of consciousness is far less appealing? Maybe that's because space is amenable to mathematical jiggery-pokery, while consciousness is not. And maybe, too, it's because the suggestion of higher worlds of consciousness includes the idea of a supreme Consciousness or Being. And that's a bit scary. It means we might be responsible, at a later date, for what we do and think. We could be subject to a natural law of causality that takes account of our thoughts and deeds. And that's definitely an uncomfortable thought for most of us. We'd rather live in an entertaining illusion than face reality.

THE RIDDLE
OF CONSCIOUSNESS

Nowadays, neuroscientists debate how immaterial consciousness arises from a material brain. But how can we ever find an answer this way, when the question and its possible answers form a seamless circle – a self-negating, insoluble conundrum? Consciousness is trying to solve the riddle of its own existence by analysing its own sensory perceptions. It is trying to understand its own nature by examining its material experience. How can consciousness understand itself in terms of its own external and peripheral experiences?

The better question to ask is how the material brain and all that it perceives in the realm of the material senses arise from an immaterial consciousness. For without consciousness, there *are* no material perceptions, there *is* no material experience.

The brain consists of water, minerals and organic substances, of atoms and molecules. And from the brain, so they say, arises consciousness. But how can consciousness arise from atoms and molecules when atoms and molecules are perceptions of consciousness?

Most scientists (though not all) reason that mind and consciousness arise from neurological activity in the brain. But maybe it is the other way around. Maybe neurological brain activity arises from the presence of mind and consciousness.

In order for us to function in this world, the mind must affect the body, and the body the mind. This means that all mental, emotional and spiritual processes and experiences – including meditation, out-of-the-body, and mystical experiences – will show up as neurological activity in the brain. But that does not mean that brain activity is the *cause* of mental processes and consciousness. That is why no amount of knowledge of the relationship between brain function and states of consciousness, including mental and emotional processes, will ever lead to an understanding of the nature and origins of consciousness. It won't help you to understand yourself. Even the science of psychology, the analysis of the functioning of the subconscious, has little basis in neuroscience.

No conceptual answer concocted by the mind regarding either itself or that of the underlying consciousness that gives it existence can ever contain the whole story. How could it? How can the knees understand the entire body? How can a part understand the whole?

The way for consciousness to understand the nature of consciousness is beyond the reasoning or intellectual faculty of the mind. Consciousness or being can only understand itself by a process of inward focus or concentration upon itself. By a process of inward expansion, of inward ascent in consciousness towards the source of consciousness – the One Being. By a different way of knowing and understanding.

113

This is nothing new to us. We are already aware that there are ways of knowing other than intellectual thought. How is it, for example, that we experience and appreciate beauty? How do we feel love and affection? Or how do we even know that we are conscious? Not by intellect or reason. The philosopher who said, "I think, therefore I am," got it wrong. The reality is, "I am, *therefore* I think."

Consciousness comes first. You need consciousness even to convince yourself that immaterial consciousness has no existence independent of material substance.

The One Being can also be called the Universal Consciousness. Our individual consciousness can only understand itself by experiencing oneness with its Source, with the Universal Consciousness, and therein lies the answer to the riddle of consciousness. Hence, the sages of ancient Greece said, "Know thyself."

This is no new idea. This way of knowing has been described by practically all the world's spiritual traditions. It is called mystic or spiritual experience. And it's not just Eastern traditions that are familiar with the experience. The ancient Greeks, and many of the early Christians knew of it, too. They called it *gnosis*.

Once it is understood that the primary reality is being or consciousness, then everything starts to fall into place. A scenario based on the idea that matter and material energy are the primary reality will always be faced with the two questions, "But where did it all come from?" and "Who is asking the questions?" The realization that everything is an expression of consciousness removes this sting from the tail. It takes us out of the realm of paradox and duality into the realm of being where everything is as it is, outside the illusion of time. Then we come to understand that ultimate 'answers' are to be found through the personal exploration of one's own consciousness, not through intellectual analysis.

And this is the nature and purpose of meditation or spiritual practice. Transcending intellect, meditation is the exploration of consciousness by consciousness itself. It doesn't supplant or invalidate scientific study. It simply places it in a wider framework. The framework of the One Being.

115

Everything we perceive with our senses is just a projected image. There is the light in the projector: that's the One Being. Then there's the film through which the light shines: that's the mind. And then there's the screen on which the projected images appear: that's this world.

And us? We are the light, of the same essence as the One Being. So we, with our minds, are a part of the projection system. We are conscious beings, and everything is a projection of the One Conscious Being, the Universal Consciousness. Switch off the light in the projector and everything disappears.

It's just an example, of course. Just a concept or perspective. So it has its imperfections. The projection system is not a static affair. It is multidimensional and supremely dynamic. And there is a progressive hierarchy of screens on which the images are projected. As the light moves out from its Source, each screen and its images become increasingly more dense and less subtle. These are the so-called higher worlds or heavens, with the final and most dense screen being the material world.

The screens themselves are also projected from the Source, as too are all the images appearing on them. So the imagery has its limitations. But maybe it gives us an idea of how everything comes into being, and how all the little beings are a part of the process by which the cosmos is projected and sustained.

What we call science is the analysis of the image that appears on the final screen, the material screen of sensory perception, of sensory experience. And the instrument of that analysis – the reasoning aspect of the mind and brain – is itself a part of the projection process, though barely distinguishable from the material screen itself.

So there is no external material world that is entirely separate from us. Our sensory experience of the material world *is* the material world. Or our personal version of it, for it's an entirely subjective experience. That's why we can never be certain that you and I have the same experience when looking at the same thing. But because we are both integral parts of the projection system (along with all the other little beings, human or otherwise), there are sufficient similarities or points of common reference in our shared experience to make us think that there is a real external world out there that we are both perceiving. In fact, we are all swimming in an ocean of being, an ocean of consciousness. And we perceive things according to the subjective mental movie that plays continuously within ourselves.

But again, it's all just a concept – a way of trying to describe the essentially indescribable. The concept is itself just another part of the dancing image on the screen.

There's another way of looking at it. Another example or concept. The One Being is the ultimate energy source, the central powerhouse. And He is conscious energy, too. Don't forget that. His energy is imbued with an intelligence and wisdom way beyond human capacity to grasp. So He projects Himself as a series of energy levels. His one energy dances outwards into a multiplicity of forms – of forms that we perceive, since we are a part of this projected energy dance. And the bottom end of this beam of energy is what we call the material world. It's nothing but a dance of energy in which we are intimately involved as participating beings.

There are strong indications in modern physics both of this energy dance and of our participation in it. For a start, when we examine matter, we find that it is intensely energetic. Nothing remains still. All material substance, however solid and stationary it may appear, is actually seething with activity at the subatomic level. Matter *is* energy, as Einstein figured out, and as we see in nuclear explosions. Yet no one can say where all this constantly available and ultradynamic energy is coming from.

120

And then there's the seemingly weird phenomenon by which the act of observation influences what is being observed. This means that nothing really has an objective state, independent of the observer. There are plenty of books covering the subject if you want to know more about that one.

So there we have it. Us and our world. A vibrant, constantly moving image projected on a screen, or a projected energy dance. And the primal light in the system or the primeval energy of the dance is the conscious light or energy of the One Being.

But these are only human concepts, spun out in the human mind. They will appeal to some, and not to others. Either way, such concepts do little justice to the actual transcendent reality of the One.

So bearing this view of things in mind, let's take a closer look at some of the fundamentals of the material universe as described by science. We can begin by examining the extraordinary way in which the 'laws of nature' seem to indicate that the very fabric of the universe supports our existence. And then we can take a peek at the supremely cooperative way in which living organisms themselves have kept our planetary biosphere habitable for hundreds of millions of years.

It's a remarkable fact, and something scientists have puzzled over for many years, but the universe itself is supremely and surprisingly biofriendly. If it wasn't just the way it is, there would be no life. And it's not just a few things that make life possible. There's a vast array of seeming coincidences that make it possible for the universe to support life. Scientists have called these coincidences utterly astonishing and by various other superlatives, for if any of them were different by no more than a hair's breadth, life itself could not exist. It seems as if the basic fabric of the physical universe is geared towards life.

It is evident in every aspect of existence. Looked at from the submicroscopic viewpoint, the physical universe is constructed almost entirely of more or less 'empty' space inhabited by a well-ordered soup of the

subatomic particles that comprise matter and its energies. If the electromagnetic and other forces between
these subatomic particles were less than they are, then
atoms, molecules, solar systems, galaxies, and indeed
the entire universe would fly apart.

If, on the other hand, these forces were much
greater, then the subatomic particles would be so
tightly compressed that the atomic and molecular
interactions required by life processes would become
impossible, like swimming in molasses – or concrete.
Electromagnetic and intra-atomic forces are all optimal
in value.

Then there's the weight of subatomic particles.
That is just right, too. Neutrons, for example, are
heavier than protons by a minuscule amount. If it were
the other way around, so physicists have calculated, the
protons would all have decayed into neutrons long ago.
And without protons, there would be no chemistry –
and no life.

Protons also carry a positive electric charge,
identical but opposite to that of the electron. There is
no apparent reason for this equality, yet were it not
so, atoms and molecules would never have formed.
In short, the detailed organization of matter at the
subatomic level is not just superlatively biofriendly, it's
essential to the very existence of the material universe.

It's the same story when you look at things from an astronomical viewpoint. First of all, there's this mysterious force we call gravity. Why should it have the particular strength it does? Why not more – or less? It is gravity that holds the universe together in a dynamic, yet stable, manner. If it were too strong, everything would fall into one massive black hole. Too weak, and no moons would travel around their planets, no planets would orbit their suns, and no suns would circulate in an orderly fashion around the black holes at the centres of their respective galaxies.

The strength of gravity also determines the optimal spacing between the stars for a life-supporting universe. If the stars were not spaced so very far apart, they would all fall into each other, or at least life would be continuously disrupted by the effect of near misses with neighbouring stars. Passing stars would rip planets out of their orbits, and generally unbalance what is actually a well-ordered universe.

In fact, the stars are more or less perfectly spaced. On a scale in which the earth is the size of a marble, our sun would be three hundred yards away. But our closest stellar neighbours would be at a distance of around forty-nine thousand miles. Stars and their planets are separated by ample space to avoid interstellar mayhem, yet not so far apart as to fly off on their own. The black holes at the centre of galaxies are shepherds to the stars, just as stars are shepherds to their planets, and planets to their moons. And the binding force is gravity. A mysterious force whose strength is entirely biofriendly.

Then there are the extraordinary properties of some of the everyday things around us. Water, for instance, exhibits unique properties possessed by no other substance. Yet without these properties, life could not exist. There is, for instance, no other liquid with the same universal capacity to dissolve and transport substances. Its role in photosynthesis – the way in which solar energy is introduced into the food cycle – is also critical. It is intimately related to the origins of all atmospheric oxygen. And the unusually large amount of heat required for its evaporation enables mammals to more easily regulate their body temperature by sweating.

Then there's its peculiar property of expanding when it solidifies. This makes ice lighter than water, with the result that it floats, helping to insulate the underlying water. But for this, ice would sink to the bottom of oceans, lakes and rivers. There, far from sunlight, it would remain, while more ice sank from the surface layers. Soon, many of the oceans, lakes and rivers of the world would be frozen so solid that even in summer they would never thaw completely. The Arctic would be solid ice right down to the ocean floor.

Erosion, too, would not proceed as rapidly. Rock is split when water freezes in the cracks, and the expanding ice fragments its surface. This and other processes – like the weakly corrosive effect of carbon dioxide, which forms carbonic acid in water – are responsible for the slow erosion of entire mountain ranges. By this process, new minerals are released to fuel the organic needs of life in the plains below. The Ozarks of south-central USA, for instance, are the remaining stubs of ancient peaks once far higher than they are today. Erosion, together with the continuous movement of the earth's crustal plates, is how the surface of the planet is continuously recycled. Without it, the earth's biosphere would be a very different place.

Then there is the remarkable correspondence between the particular electromagnetic energy emissions of our sun (and many other stars) and the photosynthetic and absorptive properties of chlorophyll. The wavelengths of solar energy correspond exactly to the way molecules are put together. There is only one such section of wavelengths in the entire electromagnetic spectrum, and chlorophyll and many of the stars have both found it, quite 'coincidentally'.

127

It is not that other substances could absorb energy from other electromagnetic wavelengths. Chlorophyll has not 'evolved' to accommodate the solar wavelengths on offer. At other wavelengths, neither chlorophyll nor other substances could capture solar energy. Too short, and they would be disintegrated as with X-rays and gamma rays. Too long, and the energy would be insufficient for absorption. The way it is, is the only way it could be to support organic life.

Then there's space itself. Space has three dimensions. Why? Why not two or four – or more? Well, two dimensions would make it impossible to get about without constant collisions. Nothing could ever go over or under anything else, for there would be no 'over' or 'under'. On the other hand, physicists have calculated that four or more spacial dimensions would create totally unstable planetary – and other – orbits. Three is just right.

No less remarkable than the biofriendliness of the universe is the way in which living organisms look after their own existence on our planet. It is not all competition and survival of the fittest. Life is also cooperative. Life supports life.

For life on earth to continue, there are a great many things that must be maintained within a very narrow range of parameters by the living organisms

themselves. Nothing can be taken for granted. It is
the living organisms that keep the planet habitable.
Without them, we'd soon end up like Mars or Venus.

Firstly, there is the balance of oxygen, nitrogen,
carbon dioxide, and other gases in the atmosphere.
Almost everyone knows that plants and trees take
carbon dioxide out of the atmosphere, using the energy
of sunlight to help incorporate the carbon into roots,
leaves and branches, while at the same time releasing
oxygen. Most other creatures breathe in oxygen, using
it to 'burn up' carbon-based substances to provide
energy for their physical existence, breathing out carbon
dioxide in the process. It sounds simple enough, but
without the maintenance of a fine balance in the relative
concentrations of these two gases, life would be impossible. Yet this balance has been maintained for hundreds
of millions of years – for as far back as indications can
be found in the geological and fossil record. Only a
little more oxygen would result in spontaneous com-
bustion of the entire carbon-based biomass. A global
conflagration, resulting in an atmosphere comprised
largely of carbon dioxide. And too much carbon dioxide
would lead to a runaway greenhouse effect, the biosphere
rapidly becoming too hot to support organic life.

A similar finely tuned balancing act applies to
the concentration of nitrogen – the element comprising

129

nearly eighty percent of our atmosphere, essential to
plant growth, and a key component of amino acids,
proteins, and much else besides. Similarly with
ozone, methane, nitrous oxide, ammonia, and other
atmospheric gases. Likewise, atmospheric pressure,
the salinity of the oceans, the recycling of essential
elements, and so on. All of these are dynamically

130 maintained in a delicate balance by the earth's living
organisms. Without living creatures, planet earth
would be very different.

We take the sea's salinity for granted. Yet, apart
from a few specialist bacteria and invertebrates, living
organisms can only exist at very low levels of salinity,
which the oceans never exceed. How so? Water runs
off the land due to rain and snowfall. Every day, it
carries millions of tonnes of minerals and debris to the
oceans. The water then evaporates, falling once again
as rain and snow upon the land. But not so the minerals. Some falls as sediment to the ocean floor or builds
up in river estuaries, but much goes into solution,
increasing marine salinity.

About 540 million tonnes of minerals in solution
reach the oceans every year. So the saltiness of the sea
should be continually increasing. But it is not. Why
not? Because armies of specialist plankton use the minerals – particularly calcium and silicon – in their shells

and 'skeletons'. When they die, they fall to the ocean floor, where they are destined to become sedimentary rock such as limestone. If there are more minerals, the plankton population increases; less minerals, and the population decreases. Every day, more than a million and a half tonnes of minerals are deposited on the sea bed, thanks to the industry of these little guys. It's a perfect biological feedback system, keeping the oceans habitable.

And not only that. A nuclear heat engine, largely powered by the decay of radioactive uranium in the earth's interior, causes continuous movement of the earth's crustal plates. This movement recycles the minerals on the ocean beds, thrusting them up as continental hills and mountains, which are again eroded, finding their way back to the sea. By erosion, mountains supply the minerals essential to life on land and in the sea. Without this constant recycling, as the mountains were all eroded away, organic life would come slowly to a halt.

Then there are elements such as iodine and sulphur, essential to so many living creatures. Why don't these elements all end up in the sea? It is because they are intercepted at the coast by seaweeds like kelp, which combine them with carbon and hydrogen, converting them into gases that blow back over the land in clouds and on-shore breezes, returning them to the earth with the falling rain. Every year, about a million tonnes of methyl iodide are recycled in this manner. Sufficient to maintain a healthy concentration of iodine in the soil, and hence in fruits and vegetables, and higher up the food chain.

And so the story continues. We could go on and on, detailing the remarkable ways in which the planetary biosphere maintains itself. Nature has many ways of keeping its own balance against the backdrop of a universe whose essential nature is biofriendly.

The fact is that everything seems to be perfectly arranged for the existence and maintenance of life. If one sees the physical universe as the ultimate and only reality, then there is no explanation for it. It is utterly astonishing. Theories of self-organization do not begin to explain the situation for they start out by accepting the material laws of nature as a done deal. But how do these laws arise? Why are things the way they are? Where does all this order, organization, and life-sustaining beneficence come from? Why should it be possible to discern any repeating trends in nature or any organization at all? Why isn't everything infinitely spontaneous and chaotic?

The truth is that scientists have no convincing answers even for the fundamental order and organization in nature, let alone the fact that this order is pro-life, and that life itself is so amazingly self-sustaining. True, it has been argued that all these factors simply represent the remarkable ability of life to adapt to circumstances. In some instances, this may be a part of the picture, but how and where does life get its remarkable capacity for such adaptation?

From a mystical perspective, from the viewpoint **133** of the One Being, there is nothing at all mysterious about it. The cosmos is well ordered and its inherent laws and principles support life because it is projected and sustained as an integrated whole from the Ocean of Life and Being itself. The fabric of the cosmos is one of order, harmony and integration because the universe is formed as a diversification of the One Harmony, the One Being into myriad parts. The same One Light illuminates all. The same One Life gives life to all. Living organisms are bound into one self-sustaining whole because their inner essence is one. They are all drops of the same Ocean of Being.

We are not amazed by the order and patterning we see in a kaleidoscope because we understand that one original pattern has been reflected and multiplied many times. The same principle lies behind the way in which the One Being projects the universe. He is the supreme Intelligence, the supreme Consciousness, and that intelligence and consciousness is projected and reflected into everything, and pervades all. And His kind of order and patterning is greater by far than that of an inert kaleidoscope. His essence is intelligence and consciousness, which are present everywhere. "Not a leaf falls but with His knowledge."

Though they find it difficult to explain, scientists readily admit to this order and organization in nature. Many, however, baulk at the notion of inherent design, especially intelligent design, because this necessarily involves a designer – a divine Designer. And because the idea has been taken on board by Christian creationists, eager to support the idea of a six-day creation event, which happened about 4000 years ago.

In many ways, however, from the non-religious and universal viewpoint of the cosmos as an emanation of the One Being, the debate over whether or not there is a designer is a non-argument. In the One Being scenario, there is no independent divine Designer. What you see is what you have. We are looking at the Designer when we see order or design. "Nature is the living, visible garment of God." And He is one with His garment. This is very different from the aloof and independent God of common religious conception. That is why I've largely avoided the God-word. The One Being is eternally present within every being and within every particle of the cosmos. Words simply fail to convey the reality.

So the universe as a projection of the One Being is naturally supportive of life or being, and the individual beings are all bound into one integrated and self-regulating whole. If everything is derived from and permeated by the One Being, how could it be otherwise? Bearing this in mind, let's now take a look at the basic fabric of the material universe, at where we are right now – in space and time. Lost in space and time, if the truth be told. So it should be worth understanding something more of their intrinsic nature.

135

SPACE, TIME AND STUFF

When we open our eyes we see nothing but space.
There are lots of other things we see in that space, like
family, friends, the dog, door knobs, buses, bushes,
fields, hills, and whatever; but primarily we see just
space. So that must be the basic reality of the world
in which we find ourselves. Space. I mean, is there
anything else out there?

And time? Well, I guess that's just how we perceive the change and movement that goes on in space.
If there was no change, no movement and difference
between things, how could you measure time?

And can change go backwards? Can you go back
in time as some scientists and fiction writers like to
think? That doesn't seem to make much sense, which
I suppose explains why we don't find bizarrely dressed,
weird-looking beings turning up in the kitchen, looking

lost, and saying they've just come from the future, and can they have some breakfast. And how far into the future? A million years? A thousand million? Still human? And what does a being from the future have for breakfast?

Or could you go back in time by a few seconds, minutes, hours, days, weeks...and meet your (slightly younger) self? And change previously made decisions with the benefit of foresight? Could you organize a party in the past, attended only by versions of yourself? Something to do just before you die? An uncomfortable thought, perhaps. Could you constantly escape death by going back in time? It may be possible in the realms of mathematics and fantasy to create such scenarios, but the concept is too impossible and bizarre to contemplate.

So there it is, space. Our reality. Ever-changing space.

And if you wanted to be one of those clever guys who try to figure out the way the world in which you find yourself is put together, I reckon that examining space itself would be the best place to start. And the more powerful the microscope, the better. You need to look at the tiny detail. But first of all, let's clear away the clutter. Let's look at some *empty* space, a vacuum. Figure out how the vacuum of space is put together, and *eureka*, you've got a handle on how the entire material universe is put together; because its primary reality is space.

And there are plenty of guys out there trying to do just that. Problem is, a microscope doesn't work at that level of detail. You need really high energy gear to look at nothing. And that should give us a clue, for a start. Nothing is not nothing if you need that kind of equipment just to look at it, or to take it apart.

139

The fact is, empty space is not empty. It's packed with energy. That's what the really clever guys have been saying for some time now. And as for the details, there are a few who have developed the maths to show that what everyone calls subatomic particles are actually little pumps or vortices, pumping or spinning energy out of the vacuum of space to make all the forms we see. Like the family, friends, the dog, door knobs, buses, and everything else.

And that's a good thing, because these guys are also in the process of figuring out how to make the energy of space do useful things in our familiar world. Like take us to work, fly us off on holiday, provide light, do the cooking, keep us warm, keep us cool, and all that sort of stuff. And – so it would seem – with no pollution either, which is definitely a good idea.

Now there's a general consensus of opinion among scientists that it should be possible to describe all the 'laws' of nature in a single theory, one grand unified theory, modestly dubbed a theory of everything. It entails combining the theories of gravitation and electromagnetism (and somehow that includes everything else). You've probably read about it in *Time* magazine or somewhere, but never really understood what they were talking about. The idea in itself is intriguing, for it indicates an acknowledgment that all of nature functions as a single whole. That there's an underlying unity in nature.

And it's interesting that at least one team among those working on the extraction of energy from space started by first formulating a single unified theory. For it turns out that all known physical 'laws' can be derived from their mathematical descriptions of the energy of space. Their theory of the way space is put together – let's call it 'space-energy theory' – accurately predicts all the known 'laws' of nature. And that includes the 'laws' of gravity and electromagnetism, together with the whole of quantum physics.

Due for publication sometime soon, their theoretical work has yet to be published, so I guess it has to be treated as speculative. But it is looking pretty good. In fact, their version of space-energy theory (there are other less complete versions) is the foundation for an entirely new take on physics, and may well provide a viable alternative to string theory, presently regarded as the only real contender as a grand unified theory.

There's a fundamental difference between the two. String theory is quintessentially conceptual. It's like philosophy using the language of mathematics. Moreover, to make the mathematics work, it requires the introduction of counterintuitive notions such as additional dimensions of space, an infinity of parallel universes, and a whole lot more. This conceptual complexity has arisen because the *reality* of the energy of space is being ignored. Like much of modern theoretical physics, string theory understands the energy of space more as an intellectual or mathematical *concept* than as something that actually exists. As something – so to speak – that you could put in a jam jar.

141

Once it is accepted that the energy of space is real, then the formulation of a single unified theory is greatly simplified. In fact, it could hardly be simpler. The foundation of the single theory is actually space itself, the energy of space. It's exactly as we see it when we open our eyes. The entire physical universe arises from and exists in space. One expanse of space. All the theory needs to do is to fill in the detail.

Of course, a theory that takes the energy structure and dynamics of space itself as the primary reality of the physical universe is still conceptual. That's what theories are. But its advantage over string theory is that it relates comfortably and intuitively to the everyday three-dimensional world in which we find ourselves. To what we perceive with our senses. And that is why, while string theory seems to be untestable in the laboratory, space-energy theory is already being applied to the possible extraction of useful energy from space.

The difference between the two theories bears some resemblance to the difference between Western and Eastern philosophy. Western philosophy (in its modern form) deals with semantics, logic, and pure reason. It is largely a conceptual and intellectual exercise. Eastern philosophy, on the other hand, is (at its best) essentially practical, dealing with the individual exploration of consciousness, approached through the practice of meditation. The former theorizes and conceptualizes; the latter tries to understand reality through experience.

The complex mathematics and speculative concepts of string theory thus reflect trends in the Western mindset. While space-energy theory, which regards the energy processes of space as something that actually exists and can even be manipulated technologically, is more in keeping with the Eastern mindset, where a clear distinction is maintained between the description and the thing described.

"What's an orange?" asks the Zen master of the eager young disciple, and the disciple sets out upon a long conceptual discourse on the nature of oranges. "No!" exclaims the master, taking an orange in his hand and squashing it firmly upon the head of his surprised disciple, "*That's* an orange!"

So space-energy theory is a fundamentally different approach. And it's interesting to speculate what effect its insights into the internal structure and dynamics of space, as the origin of all subatomic particles and forces, will have on current scientific perceptions. It will probably herald as great a shift in basic scientific understanding as the discovery that atoms have an internal structure. Something that was a major breakthrough at the time, more than a century ago. The discovery was hotly contended, too, for the atom had previously been deemed indestructible, and many physicists of the day genuinely thought that there was little more in physics to be discovered.

143

Presuming that the theory can be successfully translated into technology, a practical understanding of space-energy processes has the potential to revolutionize all aspects of science. Everything – from energy generation, to information technology, to medicine, to neuroscience and the understanding of brain function – will be seen in a new light. Maybe the brain will come to be

understood as something like a space-energy computer –
until the next major shift in scientific perception takes
place, perhaps as an integrated understanding of the
energies of mind and space.

Who knows? And who knows how far science
can go before it reaches the limits not only of intellectual understanding, but of the physical universe itself?
Or maybe there are many conceptual frameworks by
which the energy dynamics of the physical universe
can be described. And with the passage of time, we will
move on from one to another.

But whatever the concepts and theories, the question that remains unanswered is: where does all this
vibrating, dancing energy of space come from? And the
answer given by the sages is: from the Word – the Axis
of Being, the Ontological Dimension, the Tree of Life,
the cosmic Music. It's all the intelligent and conscious
energy of the One Being, dancing into created form.

We are aware that everything around us is
constantly changing. But physicists have taken things
far deeper and have shown in the laboratory that at
the most fundamental level of physical existence, the
material universe is just a dance of particles, a dance of
energy, an incredibly wonderful magic show.

The sage or mystic, looking within himself,
simply observes where all that energy is coming

from – continuously, moment by moment. New, not just every morning, but every fraction of a second. At that deep level of matter, and with the advantage of an expanded consciousness, you can watch the divine Word in action, the One Being in the act of creation.

All the things around us – the chair we are sitting on, the floor beneath our feet, everything in the space around us – is seething with the incessant activity of the divine creative process. And, so the sages say, that energy is consciousness and intelligence. Sometimes, when the day is clear and bright, and our hearts are filled with joy, we get a sense of the divine magic that surrounds us. But even more than that, so they say, the creative process can be experienced within our own being as a cosmic music far surpassing in its beauty anything created by human agency.

So here we are, lots of little beings in many guises, living in a world of changing space. We are spiritual beings dwelling in physical bodies. I look at you, you look at me, we both look at a chair. It's for sure that when you look at me, it's different from when I look at me. Because I'm a conscious being trying to look at my own being, and you're a conscious being looking at my body. Unless you are a very wise person, you can't see my thoughts and feelings, and you certainly can't experience them in the way I do. We just can't ignore this obvious fact if we want to get to the bottom of who we are, where we are, and what we are doing here.

We would appear to be on safer ground when we both look at the same thing. I look at a chair, you look at a chair. What's the problem? The problem is that we have no way of comparing our two experiences to see if they tally. Perception is subjective.

And not only that – what we perceive *is* our reality. Look at a dolphin. Under water, it uses echo location to get about. Its world is one of 3-D sonar. It perceives a world of sound that is every bit as detailed as what it sees with its eyes when above water. Or think of a bat, whose world is largely one of ultrasound, and with which it can chase and capture a fast-flying moth. Or what about a dog, and many other species, whose sense of smell (said in some cases to be over a 1000 times more sensitive than ours) provides them with a world of 3-D fragrance? And how about sharks whose world includes an awareness of the electrical nervous impulses of other creatures? Or migrating birds, to whom the stars and the earth's magnetic field are maps to help them navigate the world? Or insects, with their various exotic sensory organs, giving them a perception of electromagnetic and ultrasonic frequencies and modulations way beyond our human ken? Or bacteria, whose world includes a perception of chemicals and chemical gradients? Or a host of (to us) weird and wonderful ways in which creatures view this world?

It makes you realize that there is no such thing as a single objective material reality. We can't say that the world is the way we human beings perceive and understand it, and that other creatures perceive various bits of our human world. So what is material reality? Will the real reality please stand up!

What if there were no human beings here at all, which – so the evolutionists maintain – was the case for several billion years? And what about the time – so they also maintain – when there were no beings at all on planet earth?

If you and I inhabit worlds of our own, which we find difficult to compare, and if every other creature has a different take on material reality, can we even maintain that there is such a thing as a single objective reality?

There's another angle to this. We human beings perceive the world as a primarily visual phenomenon. But by the time light has entered the eye, been focused by the lens, has formed an inverted image on the retina, has been turned into electrical impulses in the optic nerve, and has been interpreted by the optical cortex of the brain – where is the 'original' reality? We perceive only what our brain presents to us. And since every other sense organ in ourselves and other creatures functions in a similar manner, is there any such thing as 'objective reality'? Is there any actual material reality at all?

And there's even more intriguing stuff. Look at the many experiments which show that the brain responds to events before they happen in the external world. They call it the presentiment or pre-stimulus response. For instance, the brain takes account of pictures presented at random on a computer screen, a split second *before* the picture has been presented. *Before!*

It's mind-blowing! Which way round is reality? The brain appears to have responded to an event which at that point in time had neither happened, nor had it even been decided upon by the computer. It seems to demonstrate that the event had already happened in the mind, and that our sense of it as material reality caught up a fraction of a second later. It also puts something of a dent in our notions of free will – but that's another story.

I'd say that these experiments also suggest that the mind is a separate and more subtle entity than both the brain and physical reality. That is the mystical perception of things. But most scientists don't like the idea of a 'ghost in the machine', holy or otherwise. Well, why should they always have the last word on everything? Things are the way they are, and our beliefs and opinions are not going to change anything.

The fact is that by analysing the brain in order to find the consciousness that is doing that analysis, we will be forever endlessly chasing our tails. Only when we begin to understand that the common factor in all creatures is mind and being, and that the fundamental reality of all things is being or consciousness, not material substance, will it all start to make any sense.

The One Being's primary 'unit' of creation is not made of matter. His fundamental unit is a little being, the soul, made of His own 'substance', in His own image – being or consciousness.

Every living creature is a being, a drop, so to speak, of the Ocean of Being. And every creature also has a mind 'attached' – itself a drop of the greater or universal mind – which acts as a sort of dynamic, ever-changing screen through which 'reality' is perceived. And the mind is formative. It is the mind that creates the multiplicity of changing forms. The mind consists of subtle, shifting patterns – limitations or constraints upon the essential being or consciousness within. And it is the mind that is projected outwardly or crystallized, so to speak, as a body.

151

This is what makes one species different from another – the character of the mental envelope around the soul, the mental pattern from which the physical form is manifested. And a part of that mental envelope is what we call instinct – the unconscious and mysterious mental functioning that constrains each creature to behave in the way it does. Every creature is a being, encapsulated by mind, which has taken material form as a body.

That's how beings reincarnate and transmigrate from one body to another. What a being does in one

life leaves lasting impressions on its mind, which
then precipitates or manifests as the body and destiny
to which that being is bound in subsequent lives.
Reincarnation is the result of subtle, hidden processes
of the formative mind. The mind is the means by which
the requirements of the karmic law are worked out. The
law of *karma* is actually the law of the mind – of duality,
of cause and effect, of events happening in time.

So the primary reality is one of being, not of
material substance. And beings go wherever their
minds take them. If you watch a dog or a cat, it always
has some idea in mind when it acts. The same is true
of human beings. And also of creatures such as birds,
fishes, insects, and so on, which we human beings have
such difficulty empathizing with, and understanding.

Whatever the creature, all action originates in the
mind. We only find it difficult to understand because we
do not know what it is like to be a bird or a fly or a whale.
And if we find it so difficult to understand them, imagine
how difficult they must find it, trying to understand us.

Mostly, animals seem to assume that human
beings have the same sensory perception of reality
that they have. A tiger, for example, which has a keen
sense of smell, will always approach a prey from
downwind because it presumes that the animal can
smell it. In most instances, this is a fair assumption,

but maneaters approach a human prey in the same manner, unaware that human beings can't smell them. Of course, the mind of a dog, or a bird, or an insect – heavily hemmed about by instinctive impulses, and without human language – is very different from our own, but it is present nonetheless.

Through His Word, the One Being has manifested Himself as a multitude of little beings, encased **153** in minds and bodies. Yet He remains as the unseen Reality within every being. He is the primal Source pervading everything. An understanding of the ubiquitous presence of this one universal, all-pervading Being makes it possible to comprehend many things about our otherwise confusing existence.

As human beings, we may not be able to gain a full and complete understanding of everything because the human mind is limited in its sphere of activity. But we can certainly understand something of our situation and our limitations. And so many things fall into place and are illuminated by this one central understanding of the One Being. It leads us, for example, to some interesting insights when it comes to understanding the evolutionary processes of life on earth.

A BUNCH
OF OLD FOSSILS

It's pretty clear that change is the order of the day – or of the ages. If you look at the remains they've left behind, it's obvious that millions of critters – large, small, and tiny – have come and gone over a timespan of at least hundreds of millions of years. The earth's environment changes continuously, and the creatures have changed with it. Climate change is not a new affair. It happens all the time.

But where did they all come from, and how much do they change? Well, first off, let's understand that it is the changing minds of all creatures that result in all the changing circumstances. All the little beings – all creatures – are effectively shareholders in the reality they occupy. We have all jointly thought our world into existence. That's the way the projection system of the One Being functions. The world we know and the beings in it are all a result of this divine projection system.

According to the current scientific theory of life and its origins, however, matter came out of nowhere in a big bang, a long, long time ago. That matter then self-organized itself until, one day, the first living creature came into existence due to an accidental combination of environmental circumstances such as water, chemicals, lightning, and so on. This primal microorganism then reproduced itself, and began evolving into more complex forms in response to environmental needs, powered by natural selection of the most useful of random changes in its genetic makeup.

Now there's a great deal of unproven speculation mixed up with this theory. And if we are prepared to take on board the indications that consciousness gives rise to material substance, rather than the reverse, then some of the fundamentals of this creation story begin to unravel.

For a start, being or consciousness does not come into existence through the self-organization of material substance. The sensory perception or experience of material substance is a level of consciousness of pre-existent beings. Beings come first. Without beings, there is no material substance. We've been through all this before.

Then there's this time thing. The only moment in which being exists is the present moment. The eternal now. The past and the future are illusions engendered by the very change that brings about the sense of time. Being is essentially timeless. Time, change and material substance are all illusions. Only the eternity of the present moment has any reality.

Thirdly, there's the probability factor. Even if it were somehow possible for consciousness to arise from matter, the likelihood that a primeval living microorganism with the ability to reproduce itself could somehow be created accidentally from the coincidental juxtaposition of chemical substances and physical forces is effectively zero. The spontaneous creation of a living organism would of itself be well-nigh miraculous. For it to possess the ability to reproduce as well only adds impossibility to the impossible.

157

Over the last half-century, many scientists, using advanced statistical analysis, have reached this conclusion. They simply cannot reconcile the dynamic complexity of living organisms with the underlying statistical probabilities. "The probability that random chance created life is roughly the same as the probability that a hurricane could blow through a junkyard and create a jumbo jet." It's not a lot different from the Victorian notion that mice were spontaneously generated in baskets of soiled linen. The biochemistry of even the simplest microorganism is just too incredibly complex for it to have come into being by chance.

These three considerations – the prior existence of consciousness, the illusion of time, and the probability factor – pull the rug from beneath much of the modern scientific creation story. Scientists freely admit that they struggle with the seemingly insoluble conundrum of "What existed before time began," which is inherent in the modern myth. All consideration of the fossil record, therefore, has to be understood in this light. Especially when that exceptionally patchy and incomplete record is used to speculate on the *origins*, rather than just the *history*, of life on earth.

Don't worry, I'm not going anywhere near the literal interpretation given to an ancient Mesopotamian creation allegory, originating some 3000 years ago in a culture and mindset very different from our own. The book of *Genesis* is an intriguing document from ancient times, but it needs to be understood within its own cultural context. Like many other religious texts of that period, it uses mythology to present things that are actually beyond our human understanding. Like the stories we tell children.

So let's first remove from the equation any idea that studying the geological and fossil relics of the past will reveal to us the essential nature of life, consciousness, and its origins. What then does the fossil record tell us of the history of living creatures?

Firstly, that creatures change in response to their environment. Secondly, that this process has been going on for at least hundreds of millions of years. Thirdly, that the earliest fossil records that contain a reasonably overall picture of life on earth reveal the presence of a spectrum of creatures that bears a remarkable similarity to the modern spectrum as regards their probable levels of intelligence or consciousness.

159

For the last 300 million years or so, there have been microorganisms, vegetation, invertebrates, fish, amphibians, reptiles, and probably warm-blooded, furry creatures as well. Some have changed a lot, others not so much. But if we understand these creatures as representing a spectrum of consciousness – and compare them with their modern-day counterparts – then creatures of all degrees of consciousness appear to have been present on earth for several hundred million years. Only the outward forms have changed.

And before that? Well, the fossil record – which, at its best, represents only the tiniest of a tiny fraction of the life forms that have ever lived on earth – gets increasingly patchy, as you might expect, given the tremendous geological forces that move, shift, mould, and recycle the surface of our planet.

Pushing back in time, then, until we find the beginnings of the fossil record, we reach an era more than half a billion years ago that scientists endearingly call "snowball earth" or – say those who favour a less radical scenario – "slushball earth". Either way, it was pretty chilly. The earth was so cold that it was wrapped in ice – up to a kilometre thick say the "snowball" proponents – and it had been that way for a long time. If that was indeed the case, it would have been sufficient to grind much of the surface to dust, including fossilized creatures any larger than bacteria. And that is why, perhaps, there are no fossils of anything but bacteria and a few isolated instances of invertebrates from rock more than half a million years old.

There is certainly no clear evidence that life and consciousness originated from material substance. That is an entirely speculative theory, an unsupported extrapolation of the available data into the realm of scientific mythology.

Nor is there any actual evidence of creatures of a lower order of intelligence and consciousness changing into creatures of a higher order. This is pretty difficult to demonstrate, of course, because it's not so easy to assess the intelligence of a creature from the past, even if you have its complete fossilized remains in front of you. It's problematic enough trying to figure out the degree of intelligence possessed by the living creatures of today. Even that of your friends and relatives.

But while it seems clear that some pretty radical changes of outer form have taken place (birds are probably descended from some of the dinosaurs, for instance), there is no fossil evidence of a smooth progression from microorganisms to plants, to invertebrates, to cold-blooded vertebrates, to warm-blooded vertebrates, and thence to primates. All the essential missing links have remained missing.

And human beings? Or whatever creatures represented our level of consciousness in the past? That's the most contentious issue, of course. Proponents of the 'ancient man' hypothesis cite a few ancient artefacts that suggest the presence of 'intelligent' beings such as ourselves, and which are said to date from way before the relatively recent time span generally allotted to human beings. Metal objects embedded in coal and ancients rocks, human-like footprints in ancient alluvial deposits, human skulls and skeletons from way before we are supposed to have appeared on the scene, and things like that. Mostly they are finds dating from the nineteenth and early-to-mid-twentieth centuries, and their authenticity as truly ancient relics is dubious. But even if they were genuine, the strength of the modern neo-Darwinian belief system is sufficient for them to be generally discounted as valid fossil evidence, without further consideration. Most scientists are ultra-wary of having anything to do with them anyway, since such an interest is likely to be seriously bad for their career prospects. So the question remains open, though in the minds of most, it is shut!

From a more cosmic perspective, looking at "life, the universe, and everything" as an expression of a hidden Intelligence or Being, it seems likely that there have always been creatures possessed of human-like intelligence and the potential for realizing the highest levels of divine consciousness. But that's *a priori* reasoning, of course, and actual evidence in the fossil record is slim to non-existent. Such is its nature, since it represents only the tiniest of tiny random windows onto the events of the ancient past. Even so, absence of proof is not proof of absence.

But what drives all this change? What drives evolution? From a material standpoint, it is clearly the need to survive in a competitive biosphere, and to adapt to a changing environment. Traditional Darwinism dictates that this comes about through natural selection of random genetic mutations. But looking at the well-ordered ways of nature, I have difficulty accepting that so vital a need as adaptation to changing circumstances is not covered by something cleverer than blind chance and random mutation. Genetic processes are already known to be so intricate that it would seem bizarre if one of their primary functions was left to mere opportunism.

There are already indications that bacteria and other microorganisms can adapt to changing circumstances, like the presence of antibiotics or the possibility of a new host, in ways that seem to rule out chance. These guys reproduce so rapidly that we can see adaptive evolution taking place before our eyes. So there seems no reason why genetic processes, whose finer intricacies have yet to be unravelled, should not include feedback from environmental pressures through biochemical, biophysical and neurological processes that have yet to be understood.

163

After all, it is commonly said that more than 95% of DNA is 'junk', having no useful purpose. That's a pretty rash assumption. Just because we can't see what it is up to is no reason to discount it. Perhaps part of the 'junk' is connected with a means of adaptation to environmental change. There are certainly indications that it is involved in the switching on and off of gene function. So maybe the 'junk' contains genetic memories from the past in case they are useful in the future. This would explain the occasional instances of spontaneous atavism (reversion to an ancient form) – hens' teeth and horses' toes, for example. So dinosaurs may not be as dead as we thought. There may be a dinosaur lurking in your farmyard chicken.

But however all these changes and adaptations are orchestrated, behind all the physical processes lie the patterning processes of the formative mind, projecting subtle inner mental patterns into physical reality. This is all a part of what some folk call the law of *karma*.

Maybe, as with so many other aspects of nature, there is a natural cycle going on, covering spans of millions of years. There is certainly evidence that although species are adapting and changing all the time, radically new species only appear in waves every eight million years or so. They call it the theory of punctuated equilibria. So maybe there is an ebb and flow of the universal mind that creates these evolutionary cycles – seasons of the mind, so to speak – with a 'springtime' of subtlety when new forms can more readily come into being. Maybe even the four ages of Indian and classical Greek mythology have some basis in reality. Who knows? So much of evolutionary theory is more like speculative biological history, viewed through a window of preconceived ideas.

So I'd say that the actual origin of life on earth remains a mystery. In the divine creative process, consciousness gives rise to matter, not the reverse. Mind and spirit give rise to bodies. That's a fundamental principle. Of course, that leaves open the question not only of how life got started, but of how the physical universe itself got going. And that's the final fundamental mystery to consider.

A BANGINGLY
BIG QUESTION

Looking at what all the galaxies and what not are doing right now, scientists have come to the conclusion that the physical universe started in a very big bang, a long long time ago. That's the current creation myth of the scientific worldview.

But what's the evidence? Well, for a start, everything appears to be expanding, as if it had all come out of one very small, still point. All the stars and galaxies and so on (which are believed to have formed later from all the flying debris) seem to be moving away from each other, and to have gone on evolving into supernovas, red giants, white dwarfs, brown dwarfs, neutron stars, X-ray stars, pulsars, black holes, and a host of other fascinating whizz-bangs up there. Then there's a sort of glow in the vast spaces between the stars that is believed to be heat radiation left over from the big bang.

And anyway, so the reasoning goes, how did all those stars and things get there in the first place? Everything has to start at some point in time, doesn't it? If everything came out of one still point, and has been expanding and evolving since then, they reckon that it all started about fourteen or fifteen billion years ago, and that our solar system is about four and a half billion years old. There's a lot of supporting data for these timescales too. So it's all pretty convincing stuff.

But hang on. Before the big bang, there was no time, and no space either. And we are beings, units of being, remember, drops of the great Ocean of Being, the little worlds through which He views His creation. And not only that, but our perception of the universe is a human perception, which has no greater claim to be the real material reality than that of a badger, or a bat, or a bumblebee. And those guys are definitely not into galaxies and big bangs, and all that.

Moreover, it is through Being, through consciousness, that the universe is spun into existence along the Axis of Being. Matter only exists as a part of the shared perception of beings at the material level. So can there be matter without beings to perceive it, as there would have been if things had begun with a big bang? We've been into all that, and it's pretty heady stuff!

So...umm...maybe the beings (not necessarily organic life forms at that stage), and space, and a very subtle form of matter all came into existence simultaneously, and then gradually became denser with the passage of time? And the seemingly expanding universe and the apparent afterglow of the big bang have other explanations (of which several have been suggested)? Or maybe there's some truth in the big bang scenario, but it's not the whole picture?

It's impossible to be completely certain, of course, as any honest scientist will agree. Scientific theories are always provisional, awaiting a better description of things. Big bang theory is only a speculation, which still leaves open the huge question of what was going on before the primeval pyrotechnics, before space and time began. Where did everything come from? From Nothing? From Silence? From Stillness? From pure Being? I have no quarrel with that. Being is certainly outside of space and time. But how? How does the prior existence of Being or Consciousness fit into the picture? That's the real question. And how can there be a beginning to time?

We'll go round in circles forever, of course, seeking a solution to this conundrum. But to my mind, any understanding of how the material universe came into existence has to include the principle of Being, for this is what still sustains it right now, and what gives energy to so-called empty space. The creative process is still going on. It didn't stop 14 or 15 billion years ago.

Moreover, any understanding of the origins of time and space (and all who sail in them) must include how the mind and intellect exist as well – the very faculties that are trying to do the understanding. So in the end, maybe we just have to admit that a part of Being cannot understand the whole of Being, and that the full story of our origins will always remain a mystery to human intellectual understanding.

To truly comprehend how the dance goes on, and the nature of our part in it, we need an altogether different kind of knowing that encompasses consciousness and matter, and the primal Source of it all. To really see what's going on, we have to escape from the screen of our projected reality, and find our way up the beam of light to its Source in the projector. We have got to climb the Axis of Being within ourselves. We've been here before, I think!

And so we could continue with such intellectual cogitations. Understanding that the scientific worldview is not the answer to "life, the universe and everything" but does fit comfortably within a mystical perspective is valuable because it strengthens an awareness of the sacredness of nature. And it can help, thereby, to stem the tide of destruction we have unleashed upon the planet. Science may be at odds with the myths and dogmas of religion, but not with the understanding of a more universal spirituality.

Science is only a way of looking at the material universe, a way of understanding and manipulating nature. And if some of its basic concepts are beyond your grasp, you are not alone. They are beyond the grasp of the scientists too. They are forever discussing among themselves what some of their fundamental theories actually mean! Nobody is really sure. Much of it is just hot air in the brain, spun out in a mind whose real nature is unknown. When it comes to quantum physics, for example, they say that if you think you understand it, it's a sure sign that you don't. The same is true of mysticism, of course.

It's not science itself that is to blame for all the environmental havoc. It is we human beings, utilizing the fruits of science, looking to our own personal gain, unaware of the bigger picture, who have messed things up. And while we are a social species, and need to address planetary issues in a unified global manner, the essential solution to our problems will always lie within our individual selves.

Life is a learning process. Human existence is a schoolroom. Our field of study is our own personal spiritual evolution – how to become better human beings, how to raise our spiritual consciousness. And there is, one must presume, a divine purpose hidden in this process. There must be a reason why the One Being – a being of pure love – has created a seemingly imperfect world.

Though we cannot expect it to be a reason couched in human terms, yet there must be some intention behind all the suffering and the struggle. Something to do with being sent out into the creation, of becoming forgetful of our Source, of experiencing the pain, and of turning once again to our divine home. The total experience with all its dark and light must have some intrinsic value.

So, from a higher perspective, nobody is to blame for what goes on here. "All the world's a stage," an illusion. It has no lasting reality. The One Being has written – is continuously writing – the entire script and has created all the actors. His purpose is not a human purpose, but something way beyond our ken. He has made one man a genius, another a fool; one a tyrant and a murderer, another the fierce upholder of justice and human rights. A balance is played out between dark and light, and the game goes on.

173

The One Being is a dramatist who has even made some of the actors abuse Himself. He is a general who has command of both the armies, whose soldiers are living beings, parts of Himself that can realize the Whole. That's an essential aspect – perhaps the primary purpose – of His game.

In the total scheme of things, even physical death has no significance. The soul travels on. Good and evil, death and rebirth are two sides of the single coin of separation from the Divine. Death is essential for there to be new life. No physical body lives forever. Sooner or later it will fall apart. And so we all go round and round in the cycle of death and rebirth until the suffering becomes too much and we heed the homeward call, the beacon beckoning us to the Light.

This does not mean that there is no place for compassion, understanding, goodness, service to others. On the contrary, the game requires the utmost effort to play it well, to play it in such a way that the game may be ended. To play it with love, and rise way beyond it, back to the Source, the One Being at the heart of all. "Live in such a way that when you die, you laugh and others cry."

It is through aspiring to the heights of true humanity, to perfection while living in the midst of material temptation and distraction, that we gain the strength and purity to make the journey home. Then we can pass safely, and without getting sidetracked, through all the heavenly realms, worlds of being of indescribable beauty and fascination. Human weaknesses or imperfections are such simply because they blind us to the Divine, and bind us to the mind and body. They are mental and physical habits that attach us to this world, a misdirection of a divine gift.

All human faculties have a positive purpose and a negative potential. Human perfection means perfect control of all our faculties and potentialities; to use them to their full extent while we live as human beings, but without getting distracted from our spiritual path.

We think we are simply human beings, but actually we are spiritual beings caught up in a human experience. A drop of the Ocean of Being temporarily trapped in a human body in which our perception of what is happening is severely restricted. Yet, as human beings, our deepest instinct is to seek the Truth. Our quest, therefore, must surely be to rediscover our inherent spirituality; to escape the prison of materiality; to find once more the One Being within ourselves; to remember who and what we really are.

If, in the grand scheme of things, the life of a human being has a purpose, it is only to experience the presence of the Divine, of the Sacred. To come to know the Being who permeates both our inner being and the seemingly outer universe.

But how can we realize this inner presence? By letting go. "Let go, and let God." By realizing that He has been there all along. By stilling the otherwise interminable flow of thoughts, and focusing our awareness on the being that we are, not on the ceaseless activity of our minds. Our preconceptions, our discursive thinking, our worries about the past, our concerns for the future, our emotions and desires, our continuous preoccupation with our individual selves and with the things of time – all these have absorbed the attention of our inner being to such an extent that we have become forgetful of the One Being within, of the divine Life or Consciousness that gives us our existence. We have become forgetful of who we truly are.

But to let go of all of this, to reconnect with our innermost being, to remember the One Being, to find the One within, requires great effort. Paradoxically, for life to become effortless, striving is essential. The old adages are true: everything worthwhile demands effort. Practice makes perfect. In this case, spiritual practice, meditation or interior prayer.

It's a rare soul who finds themselves in the divine presence spontaneously and without effort. Mindfulness or remembrance of the Divine requires constant vigilance to keep the attention focused on the innermost essence of being, to retain awareness of our own essential being. Not to be continuously carried away on the current of thought and emotion, but to remain conscious and aware. This is the soul's response to the divine call, and He is forever waiting for us to turn to Him. Indeed, He is the one who prompts us from within, and makes us turn.

We already have everything we need, here and now, in the sacred present, the eternal now, within our own being. The One Being is always with us, never far. "Closer is He than breathing, and nearer than hands and feet." "Welcome the divine eternity in the passing shadows of time. Shadows that change, though the eternity they hide is changeless."

The divine Beloved is our guide, drawing us ever on. Our effort is simply a response to His call. "If we take one step towards Him, He takes a hundred steps towards us." And He is the one who makes us take that one step. His grace is inestimable, His love incalculable. We live in it, could not exist without it. If our attention is distracted and we turn our back on it, we may think He has gone away. But He is always present. There is nowhere else for Him to go. He is helpless in His love for us, united by the bond of shared and indistinguishable being.

So, to find Him is the eternal quest, the only journey worth travelling with all our heart and soul. To remain seekers until the journey's end. Never to give up, to remain positive, to let go of despondency and negativity, and become aware of the One.

It is in the simplest things that we discover that He is always there. We can find Him in nature, in the garden, in the kitchen, in the office, in our family and social life. He is present in a war zone, too, and in the extremities of disharmony and distress. He is in the smiling face and twinkling eyes of an old friend, in the antics of a child at play. He is in the poor man and the wealthy, the sinner and the saint. He takes on myriad

177

disguises in the people and events that come our way. A king hidden in the rags of humanity, even with all its imperfections; in the beauties of nature, despite the constant competition for survival.

He is never apart from His creation. He is always there, within every little being, every soul. It can never be said enough, never recalled enough, never lived enough. He is in the present moment, right now. He is within. He is without. Whenever the mind is quiet, we will find Him in our being. He is the "wind beneath our wings". He is not what we think; He is what we are.

AND FINALLY

CREATION HYMN

Neither being nor Non-being existed then;
Neither was there air, nor the heavens beyond.
What breathed? Where? In whose care?
Was water there, unfathomably deep?

There was neither death nor immortality then;
Of night and day, there was no sign.
The One breathed, without breath,
By Its own impulse:
Besides It, nothing else existed.

Darkness was wrapped in darkness then:
All was one unruffled sea.
Then the One, hidden in void, stirred, came forth:
Through fervour, came to be.

A desire came upon the One in the beginning:
The primal seed of mind.
Seers, seeking with wisdom within themselves,
Found the link between being and Non-being.

A line distinguished the one from the other –
What was below? What above?
There were seed-sources,
There were generative powers:
There was impulse from beneath,
There was giving birth above.

Who really knows? Who can tell the tale?
How did it all arise? Whence this creation?
Even the gods came later, after it was formed.
Who, then, can tell how it has come to be?

None knows whence this creation has arisen –
Whether He made it or whether He has not –
He who surveys it from the highest heaven:
Only He knows; or maybe He does not....

Thanks, firstly, to all those who helped get this book into shape. Of the quotations, "Rabbit's clever..." is from A.A. Milne's *Winnie the Pooh,* and "All the world's a stage" was already a common saying when Shakespeare used it to start a famous soliloquy in *As You Like It.*

"I think, therefore I am" was Descartes. The full quote is, "I doubt, therefore I think, therefore I am." "Nature is the living..." was Goethe. "The probability that random chance..." is one of a number of variants of a quip credited to the astronomer, Fred Hoyle.

"Closer is He than breathing..." was Alfred Lord Tennyson. "Welcome the divine eternity in the passing shadows of time..." was François de Sales. "Off and on, in some rare moments..." is from the Indian scholar, philosopher, and president (1962–67), S. Radhakrishnan.

The "wind beneath our wings" takes mild poetic
licence with the song title, "Wind Beneath My Wings" by
Larry Henley and Jeff Silbar. "Music for a While (shall all
our cares beguile)" is a song by the seventeenth-century
composer, Henry Purcell. Two great songs!

"When He decrees a matter...", "Not a leaf falls...",
"all the worlds", "the best of forms", "Be!" and "Return!"
are all from the *Qur'an*. "Die before you die" is a saying
attributed to the Prophet Muhammad in the Muslim
tradition. "I was a hidden treasure..." is also from the
Muslim tradition. "Live in such a way..." is a Sufi saying.

The "image of God" appears in both the Bible
and the *Qur'an*. "In the beginning was the Word...",
"Word made flesh", "Be ye therefore perfect", "My
yoke is easy...", "many mansions", "legion, for we are
many", and "possessed with demons" are all from the
Christian gospels.

"Cool as sandalwood..." is from the poetry of
the Indian mystic, Paltu Sahib, and the "divine human
body" is also from the Indian mystics. The creation
hymn that forms the epilogue is the *Nasadiya Sukta* of
the *Rig Veda*, written around 500 BCE.

"The name that can be named..." is how Lao Tzu
opens the *Tao Te Ching*.

"Know thyself" is a Greek aphorism of the
classical period, attributed to a number of the ancient

sages, and appearing as an inscription in the forecourt of the Temple of Apollo at Delphi. The single general in command of two opposing armies and the playwright whose characters abuse him are images from Plotinus – a third-century, Neo-Platonist mystic.

The team working on the extraction of energy from the vacuum of space, who have developed a new form of space-energy theory unifying all known physical laws and processes, is led by Doug Torr. Part of his theoretical work, in association with José Vargas, is presently scheduled for publication, probably in 2010, with more to follow. Of course, their work still requires the scrutiny of their fellow scientists, but both are respected, published physicists, who have been working in this area for several decades.

185

"We pronounce it 'I', as if it were the whole of us...", "He worships Himself through us", and "If we take one step..." are from Maharaj Charan Singh, my spiritual master, and primary source of inspiration.

"The Answer to Life, the Universe, and Everything" is the Ultimate Question put to the computer 'Deep Thought' in Douglas Adams' *The Hitchhikers' Guide to the Galaxy*. Deep Thought took 72 million years to figure out the answer, which, as everyone knows, is 42.

BOOKS BY SSRC

BOOKS ON MYSTICISM
A Treasury of Mystic Terms,
Part I: The Principles of Mysticism (6 volumes)
– John Davidson
One Being One – John Davidson

PERSONAL EXPERIENCE
A Soul's Safari – Netta Pfefier
Adventure of Faith – Shraddha Liertz

VEGETARIAN COOKBOOKS
Baking Without Eggs
Creative Vegetarian Cooking
The Greenway to Healthy Living
Meals with Vegetables

ORIGINS OF CHRISTIANITY-
– John Davidson
The Gospel of Jesus
The Divine Romance
The Odes of Solomon
The Prodigal Soul
The Song of Songs

BOOKS BY RSSB

SOAMI JI MAHARAJ
Sar Bachan Prose (The Yoga of the Sound Current)
Sar Bachan Poetry (Selections)

BABA JAIMAL SINGH
Spiritual Letters

MAHARAJ SAWAN SINGH

The Dawn of Light
Discourses on Sant Mat
My Submission
Philosophy of the Masters, in 5 volumes
Spiritual Gems
Tales of the Mystic East

MAHARAJ JAGAT SINGH
Discourses on Sant Mat, Volume II
The Science of the Soul

MAHARAJ CHARAN SINGH
Die to Live
Divine Light
Light on Saint John
Light on Saint Matthew
Light on Sant Mat
The Master Answers
The Path
Quest for Light
Spiritual Discourses, in 2 volumes
Spiritual Heritage
Thus Saith the Master

BOOKS ABOUT THE MASTERS
Call of the Great Master – Daryai Lal Kapur
Heaven on Earth – Daryai Lal Kapur

Treasure Beyond Measure – Shanti Sethi
With a Great Master in India – Julian P. Johnson
With the Three Masters, in 3 volumes – Rai Sahib Munshi Ram

INTRODUCTION TO SPIRITUALITY
A Spiritual Primer – Hector Esponda Dubin
Honest Living – M. F. Singh
The Inner Voice – C. W. Sanders
Liberation of the Soul – J. Stanley White
Life is Fair: The Law of Cause and Effect – Brian Hines

BOOKS ON MYSTICISM
The Holy Name: Mysticism in Judaism – Miriam Caravella
Jap Ji – T. R. Shangari
Yoga and the Bible – Joseph Leeming

BOOKS ON SANT MAT IN GENERAL
In Search of the Way – Flora E. Wood
Living Meditation: A Journey beyond Body and Mind
  – Hector Esponda Dubin
Message Divine – Shanti Sethi
The Mystic Philosophy of Sant Mat – Peter Fripp
Mysticism: The Spiritual Path, in 2 volumes – Lekh Raj Puri
The Path of the Masters – Julian P. Johnson
Radha Soami Teachings – Lekh Raj Puri

MYSTICS OF THE EAST SERIES
Bulleh Shah – J. R. Puri and T. R. Shangari
Dadu: The Compassionate Mystic – K. N. Upadhyaya
Dariya Sahib: Saint of Bihar – K. N. Upadhyaya
The Teachings of Goswami Tulsidas – K. N. Upadhyaya
Guru Nanak: His Mystic Teachings – J. R. Puri
Guru Ravidas: The Philosopher's Stone – K. N. Upadhyaya
Kabir: The Great Mystic – Isaac A. Ezekiel
Kabir: The Weaver of God's Name – V. K. Sethi
Mira: The Divine Lover – V. K. Sethi
Saint Namdev – J. R. Puri and V. K. Sethi

Saint Paltu: His Life and Teachings – Isaac A. Ezekiel
Sarmad: Martyr to Love Divine – Isaac A. Ezekiel
Sultan Bahu – J. R. Puri and K. S. Khak
Tukaram: The Ceaseless Song of Devotion – C. Rajwade
Tulsi Sahib: Saint of Hathras – J. R. Puri and V. K. Sethi

BOOKS FOR CHILDREN
The Journey of the Soul – Victoria Jones
One Light Many Lamps – Victoria Jones

For Internet orders, please visit: www.scienceofthesoul.org

For book orders within India, please write to:

Radha Soami Satsang Beas
BAV Distribution Centre, 5 Guru Ravi Dass Marg
Pusa Road, New Delhi 110005

OTHER BOOKS BY THE AUTHOR

ON SCIENCE AND MYSTICISM
Subtle Energy
The Web of Life
The Secret of the Creative Vacuum
Natural Creation and the Formative Mind
Natural Creation or Natural Selection?

ON CHRISTIAN ORIGINS
The Robe of Glory